WITH KEY

Landmark

Upper Intermediate Workbook

Simon Haines & Barbara Stewart

OXFORD

UNIVERSITY PRESS

Introduction	How to use this book Page 4			

1
 	
Pages 6–11
	Reading Page 6
	
	White riot
	  A newspaper article about white water rafting
		Vocabulary Page 8
		
		Phrasal verbs:
		  turn up, set off, break up
		Word groups
		Topic vocabulary: smoking
			Grammar Page 9
			
			1 Present tenses review
			2 Aspect
			3 Action verbs and state verbs
			
			► Language commentary
			  Student's Book p.124
				Writing Page 11
				
				Making writing interesting (1): adjectives and adverbs
				Describing an incident

2
 	
Pages 12–17
	Reading Page 12
	
	Sungura
	  Extract from a short story by Tracey Lloyd
		Vocabulary Page 14
		
		Topic vocabulary: eating, drinking, talking
		Phrasal verbs:
		  get away, come off, take over
		Collocations:
		  verb + noun
			Grammar Page 15
			
			1 Past simple and Past continuous review
			2 Past perfect
			3 *used to, would*
			  Past tenses
			
			► Language commentary
			  Student's Book p.125
				Writing Page 17
				
				Using correct punctuation
				Describing a personal experience

3
 	
Pages 18–23
	Reading Page 18
	
	Could global warming sink your holiday plans?
	  A newspaper article about the effects of global warming
		Vocabulary Page 20
		
		Topic vocabulary: the environment
		Phrasal verbs:
		  bring + particle
		Word-building
			Grammar Page 21
			
			1 Futures review
			  will
			  will and *going to*
			2 Future continuous and Future perfect
			  Future forms
			3 The language of contrast
			
			► Language commentary
			  Student's Book p.126
				Writing Page 23
				
				Topic sentences
				Describing a holiday resort

4
 	
Pages 24–29
	Reading Page 24
	
	Mother
	  Extract from a short story by Judah Waten
		Vocabulary Page 26
		
		Phrasal verbs:
		  go, give, throw, put, take + *away*
		Topic vocabulary: ways of looking
		Word-building
			Grammar Page 27
			
			1 Rules, needs, duties, and advice review
			2 Prohibition/no obligation
			  Mixed patterns
			3 Speculating about past events
			
			► Language commentary
			  Student's Book p.127
				Writing Page 29
				
				Making writing interesting (2): adjectives, describing a person
				Writing a description

5
 	
Pages 30–41
	Reading Page 30
	
	Death of denim?
	  A newspaper article about the jeans industry
		Vocabulary Page 32
		
		Topic vocabulary: employment
		Phrasal verbs:
		  get + particle
			Grammar Page 33
			
			1 Conditionals review
			2 The verb *wish*
			3 Mixed conditional sentences
			4 Past verbs with present or future meaning
			  It's time
			  I'd rather
			
			► Language commentary
			  Student's Book p.128
				Writing Page 35
				
				Connecting ideas (1)
				Describing similarities and differences between people

6
 	
Pages 36–41
	Reading Page 36
	
	When you hit your career peak
	  A newspaper article about the age at which people reach the peak in different professions
		Vocabulary Page 38
		
		Word-building
		Topic vocabulary: stages of life
		Phrasal verbs:
		  bring up, make up, take up, break down
			Grammar Page 39
			
			1 Present perfect review
			2 Present perfect continuous (1)
			  Present perfect simple and continuous
			3 Present perfect continuous (2)
			  Past simple and Present perfect tenses
			
			► Language commentary
			  Student's Book p.130
				Writing Page 41
				
				Expressing an opinion: adverbs
				Giving an opinion

The twelve units in this Workbook will help you
- develop your reading skills
- increase your vocabulary
- consolidate your grammar
- improve your writing.

Each unit has four parts.

Reading

You will read a variety of authentic texts, from magazine and newspaper articles to excerpts from stories. Each text is followed by questions which check your understanding. There is also work to focus on the vocabulary used in the text.

Vocabulary

This section always includes topic vocabulary, phrasal verbs, and at least one other practice exercise.

Grammar

This section contains a variety of exercises which will give you extra practice of the grammar which you have studied in the Student's Book.

Writing

In this section there are examples of different types of writing, from descriptions and biographies to letters and accounts. The writing sections in the Student's Book focus on different styles of writing, and the exercises in the Workbook focus on how to improve your writing. Each unit looks at a different aspect of writing (for example, how to make your writing more interesting, how to connect your ideas) and includes analysis, practice, and a final task.

How to use this workbook: a step by step guide

This Workbook can be used alongside the Student's Book as a source of supplementary classroom material. It can also be used for self-study; all the activities have been designed so they can be used by people working on their own.

■ Reading ■

The activities in this section will help you to develop your reading skills and your vocabulary.

Before you read

This section introduces the topic and prepares you for reading the text. Sometimes there are specific questions for you to answer (for example, True/False). Sometimes there are questions on vocabulary which you will need to know in order to understand the text. If you are working on your own you will find it useful to think about these questions before you read the text.

As you read

There is always a task for you to do as you read the text for the first time. For example, you may be asked to check your answers to the prediction exercise in **Before you read**.

Glossary

This contains words which are important for understanding the text but which are unusual or difficult.

> **Study tip**
> Don't use a dictionary as you read and don't worry about understanding every word. It is more important to get a general idea of what the text is about the first time you read it.

Focus on vocabulary

These exercises deal with some of the useful vocabulary in the text. You may already have guessed the meaning of these words from their context when you read the text for the first time. The first exercise checks that you understand what they mean; the second exercise gives you practice in using the words correctly. If you prefer, you can do the practice exercises after the questions which check your understanding of the text.

> **Study tip**
> The words in this section are useful and worth learning. It's a good idea to write them in your vocabulary book or file under appropriate headings.

Understanding the text

When we read we have to understand what the writer wants to say and interpret his or her message. This section contains different types of question. Some of these are ordinary comprehension questions, which check your understanding of the text. Others are interpretation questions, which are designed to help you to 'read between the lines'. The interpretation questions do not have a right or wrong answer. You will need to use your own ideas as well as the information in the text to answer them.

Comprehension

This heading covers two different types of activity. The first checks your general understanding and has questions about vocabulary or the ideas in the text. The second type of activity, missing sentences, is in Units 5 and 11. Some sentences have been removed from the text. You have to indicate where they go. This type of exercise tests your understanding of how the text holds together. It comes before the **Focus on vocabulary** section and we recommend that you do the activities in this order.

Study tip
Look for clues in the parts of the text which come before and after the gap. Look for words which are repeated or words which have a similar meaning. Look for reference words like *it*, *they* and *this*, which usually refer back to something mentioned in the previous sentence.

■ Vocabulary

The exercises in this section are designed to extend and reinforce your vocabulary. You can do them in any order you choose. Instead of working systematically through the vocabulary and grammar sections, you might prefer to 'mix and match'. Do a vocabulary exercise followed by a grammar exercise followed by another vocabulary exercise.

The phrasal verbs which are dealt with in the workbook are ones which you are expected to know at upper intermediate level. It is not a comprehensive selection; this would be almost impossible. At the back of this workbook there is a complete list of all the phrasal verbs which appear in the vocabulary sections, and an explanation of the grammar of phrasal verbs.

Study tip
We recommend that you transfer useful vocabulary from these exercises to your vocabulary notebook or file. Review all your vocabulary regularly. Test yourself or work with a friend and test each other. For ideas about learning vocabulary see *Learning new vocabulary* in the Student's Book, page 50.

We also recommend that you buy an English-English dictionary, if you haven't already got one . There are many good dictionaries available, for example, the *Oxford Advanced Learner's Dictionary, the Oxford Wordpower Dictionary*. For tips on using a dictionary see *Using a dictionary* in the Student's Book, page 30.

■ Grammar

The exercises in this section give you extra practice of the grammar in the Student's Book. We suggest that you do the Workbook exercises after you have studied the grammar point in class. Don't forget to use the Language commentary in the Student's Book.

Study tip
Don't try to do all the grammar exercises at once. Do one section at a time.

Vary how you do the grammar sections. You could read the relevant section in the *Language commentary* in the Student's Book first, then do the related exercises in the Workbook. Or, you could test yourself to see how much you know: do the exercises in the Workbook first and then look at the *Language commentary* if you make mistakes.

■ Writing

This section is divided into three main parts: reading an example text, focus on particular features, preparation for writing.

In the first part there are usually questions for you to answer before you read the text, and a task for you to do as you read it. It is not necessary for you to understand every word of the text. It has been chosen to introduce the topic and to show particular features of writing.

The second part focuses on what makes a piece of writing effective. It looks at a variety of features, ranging from the use of descriptive adjectives to appropriate ways of connecting ideas. You are asked to find examples of particular features in the text, and you are given practice in using them effectively.

The final part is a writing task, with suggestions on how to approach the writing. The tasks are usually short – one or two paragraphs – and give you a further opportunity to practise using the features you have just studied.

Study tip
The best way to improve your writing is little and often. The more you write, the easier it will become.

Write your task one day and look at it again the next day before you make your final version. You will find it easier to decide how effective it is if you look at it with 'fresh' eyes.

Ask a classmate to read it and give you their opinion.

1

Reading

Before you read

You are going to read an article in which the writer describes his first experience of white-water rafting.

1 Why do you think people do it? Would you like to try it?

....

....

2 Match the words from the article (a–e) with the numbers on the photograph (1–5).

a raft	b paddle	c lifejacket
d rapids	e rocks	

3 Underline the words you think you might find in the article. Use a dictionary to check any words you are not sure of.

a guide (person)	reassuring	
instructions	trapped	scream (vb)
washing-machine	sink (vb)	
paddled	truck	hospital

Glossary

tread (line 1): walk
fine line (line 1): narrow division between two different states
shoot the rapids (line 2): travel quickly through the rapids in a boat
disclaimer form (line 5): written statement in which sb says they do not take responsibility for sth
bear no liability (line 8): accept no legal responsibility
dunk (line 29): put sb or sth briefly in water
gibber (line 42): speak fast and in a way that no one can understand because you are afraid
roll-up (line 47): cigarette made by hand
whoop (line 59): give a loud cry of joy or excitement

White riot

1 MICHAEL HANLON **treads the fine line between having fun and fearing for his life as he shoots the rapids in Virginia's New River Gorge.**

2 'This is America; there's no way they'll let us get injured,'
5 said my friend Andrew shortly before the longest disclaimer form I had ever seen was pushed in front of our noses. We were about to embark on a day of white-water rafting. 'The company shall bear no liability for any injuries whatsoever,' he read. *We signed anyway.*

3 The New River Gorge national park in West Virginia is an out-of-the way spot in the heart of the Appalachian mountains. Along with the nearby Gauley River, the New River is rated as one of the best places for rafting and canoeing in the whole of the US. A number of companies
15 offer day-long white-water trips through the rapids. We picked one at random from a tourist office in nearby Beckley, and turned up at 8 a.m. as requested.

4 The inflatable rafts seat eight people and you are equipped with a lifejacket and a paddle. Our guide, an
20 amiable, chain-smoking chap called Scott clearly lived and breathed rafting, *which was reassuring.* Less reassuring were our fellow rafters. We soon realised that *they had as much experience of rafting as we did.*

5 We set off. After twenty minutes or so the river narrowed
25 from a lazy pool to a 100-yard channel between wooded cliffs; the surface started to break up. *We were being given frantic instructions* by our guide, who despite his chaotic appearance knew what he was doing. How to turn the raft left, how to stop, how to avoid a dunking and what to do if
30 you fell out (lie on your back; don't let your legs get trapped by a rock). The most important thing was to paddle like crazy through the turbulence, otherwise the raft would get trapped in a standing wave and we would get dragged under.

6 You don't see rapids before you hit them. The front of
35 the raft tips downwards, everyone screams, and suddenly *you are in a washing-machine.* Water, water everywhere. You have to hang on with your feet, wedged in under the inflatable seats. Scott shouted, 'Fore!' What did that mean? We paddled like crazy and *incredibly* the raft failed to sink.

---

1 What does this tell us about Michael, the writer, and his friend Andrew?

2 What was reassuring? Why was it reassuring?

3 How much experience did they all have? How might this affect the trip?

4 Why were the instructions 'frantic'?

5 What does this expression mean?

6 What does the word 'incredibly' tell us?

7   'That was a class one, real easy. Coming up is a class three.' We gibbered. Rocks the size of houses were approaching rapidly. 'If you fall

45   out, try to keep your head above water and swim to the <u>left</u> bank,' said Scott. 'If you swim to the right, you probably won't make it.' His roll-up was still dry.

8   The raft tipped again, this time at

50   a 45-degree angle. We slid down a 10-foot wave, avoided the rocks, and ran straight into another one. Strange pressures and vacuums pulled us this way and that. Scott

55   yelled; we paddled. The raft filled with water. After a couple of seconds – it felt like minutes – we shot out of the rapid. Everyone whooped, *even the English, to whom whooping does*

60   *not come naturally.*

9   After lunch on the river bank *we were ready for a class five*, defined as 'extremely long, obstructed or very violent rapids which expose a

65   paddler to above average danger'. Just like a class three really, but wetter. One of the rafters – a guy from Minnesota – fell out. We all joined in the effort to haul him back in.

10   The last rapid was rated 'swimmable'. Andrew and I jumped out. 'Keep to the left of the rock,' shouted Scott as we drifted away in the current, 'or you might be pulled

75   under.' The water was cold and the lifejacket made swimming difficult. My friend disappeared round the right of the rocks, so *I was pleasantly surprised to see him reappear on the*

80   *other side.* Eventually the landing stage came into view, and we were hauling the boat back on the truck.

11   White-water rafting is not for everyone – the danger is real, and

85   you need to be a confident swimmer and in fairly good shape. *But if you are prepared to live with the risks, it is harder to think of a more exhilarating day out.*

The Independent

---

7 Why don't the English normally 'whoop'? What kind of character have they got?

8 In what way were they 'ready'?

9 Why was the writer surprised?

10 Did the writer enjoy the experience?

As you read

1 Read the text once through quickly to get a general idea of what it is about and to check your predictions to **3** opposite.

2 Read the text again. This time answer questions 1–10 about the parts in italics as you read.

Comprehension

1 The following adjectives could all be used to describe the guide. Underline the expressions in the paragraphs which illustrate the adjectives.

obsessive (4)   untidy and competent (5)   relaxed (7)

2 Match the feelings and emotions which the writer experiences during the day (a–d) with the paragraph which describes them (4, 7, 8, 10).

a ☐ relieved   c ☐ exhilarated
b ☐ apprehensive   d ☐ terrified

Focus on vocabulary

The words in the list are informal expressions from the text. The paragraph number is given in brackets. Rewrite the sentences below, replacing the formal expression in italics with its informal equivalent from the list. Make any other necessary changes.

out-of-the-way (3)   make it (7)
turned up (3)   this way and that (8)
chap (4); guy (9)   a couple of (8)
or so (5)   in fairly good shape (11)
like crazy (5)

1 She was born in a *remote* place in Western Australia.
She was born in an out-of-the-way place in Western Australia.

2 When Peter saw the bull coming towards him he ran *as fast as he could*.
....

3 Andrew's uncle is *quite fit* for a man of seventy.
....

4 The new boss seems to be quite a nice *man*.
....

5 I'll be there in *approximately* ten minutes.
....

6 Julia *arrived* half an hour late as usual.
....

7 Can I ask you *a few* questions?
....

8 The strong current pulled the swimmer *in all directions*.
....

9 It was a terrible journey but they finally *arrived*.
....

Vocabulary

Phrasal verbs: *turn up, set off, break up*

1 Many phrasal verbs have more than one meaning. Use the example sentences (1–9) to help you to match the verbs with their meanings (a–i).

1 ☐ We *turned up* at 8 a.m. as requested.
2 ☐ Could you *turn up* the radio a bit please?
3 ☐ 'I can't find that report you wanted.' 'Don't worry! It'll *turn up* eventually.'
4 ☐ We *set off*. After twenty minutes or so the river narrowed.
5 ☐ If someone tries to open this door, it'll *set off* the alarm.
6 ☐ The children *were setting off* firecrackers in the streets.
7 ☐ The surface of the river started to *break up*.
8 ☐ In July most schools *break up* for six weeks.
9 ☐ Josie's parents *have broken up* after twenty-five years of marriage.

a be found (after being lost)
b make explode
c (for schools, etc.) begin the holidays
d arrive
e end a relationship
f start a journey
g increase the volume
h divide or become divided into smaller parts
i make an alarm ring

2 Check your answers. Then complete the sentences with one of the phrasal verbs above in an appropriate form.

1 Either .... the TV .... or make less noise. I want to hear the news.
2 We .... the week before Christmas. The new term starts on January 7th.
3 He looked for the book for hours, then it .... on David's desk.
4 John and Patricia .... after Patricia saw him kissing another girl.
5 Although we .... for school in plenty of time, we arrived late.
6 You can't feed a baby big pieces of food. You need to .... them .... first.
7 It's easy for the wind to .... car alarms.
8 I hadn't invited him to my party but he .... anyway.
9 It is safer if professionals .... fireworks.

Word groups

1 The four words in each group all have something in common but one is slightly different from the others. Decide which one it is.

1 grapefruit (pear) lemon orange
2 lift haul pull drag
3 rowing boat raft canoe liner
4 upright downwards sideways backwards
5 swim drift float sink

2 Choose the most appropriate word in italics in the sentences.

1 He *swam / drifted* quickly across the river.
2 The boat completely filled with water and so it *sank / floated*.
3 She looked *sideways / downwards* to see if I was enjoying the film as much as she was.
4 James paddled the *canoe / rowing boat* expertly across the lake.
5 It was so heavy they had to *lift / haul* it out of the water.
6 Stand *backwards / upright* with your back against the wall.
7 The film star entered, *hauling / dragging* her furs along the floor behind her.

Topic vocabulary: smoking

1 Match six of the words below with the drawings. Check the meanings of any words you are not sure of.

☐ addictive   ☐ put out / extinguish   ☐ non-smoker
☐ inhale   ☐ passive smoking   ☐ ex-smoker
☐ light   ☐ chain smoker   ☐ cut down
☐ roll-up   ☐ heavy smoker   ☐ nicotine
☐ ashtray   ☐ quit / give up   ☐ filter tip
☐ crave   ☐ low tar

2 Read the extracts from a health pamphlet on smoking. Fill the gaps with one of the words or word combinations from the list in **1**. Make any necessary changes.

SMOKING KILLS!

40% of .... [1] (those smoking over 20 cigarettes a day) die before retirement age, compared to only 15% of .... [2] (those who have never smoked).

Now, thankfully, people are more aware of the health hazards and women, like men, are choosing to .... [3] smoking.

Tobacco smoke is packed with poisons that can damage the heart and blood vessels. .... [4] are just as bad for you in the long run as roll-ups.

It has been shown that .... [5] (inhaling other people's smoke) can shorten life. Wives of husbands who smoke, for example, die younger than wives of non-smokers.

Set a date, prepare a plan of action, and stop. Trying to .... [6] rarely works. Filter tips and low tar cigarettes are not much help either. Most smokers cheat by smoking more or .... [7] more deeply.

Because nicotine is .... [8], you will probably experience withdrawal symptoms such as irritability and restlessness.

The evening before, smoke your last cigarette and make sure you have none left. Smoke them all or throw them away. Get rid of lighters, ... [9], and anything that reminds you of smoking.

Identify times when you particularly .... [10] a cigarette and make sure you have something to occupy your hands (worry beads, a pencil to doodle with, sewing!)

3 Write a questionnaire on smoking. Try to use as many of the words in **1** as you can.

Grammar

1 Present tenses review

1 Choose the correct form, Present simple or Present continuous. Both are possible in one case.

More and more people *take up / are taking up* cycling. When we cycle, we *use up / are using up* more energy than when we *walk / are walking*. Cycling *improves / is improving* our aerobic fitness, too.

I *go / am going* cycling regularly, but only on Sundays when the roads are quieter. Then, I *drive / am driving* into the country, I *park / am parking* the car and I *pedal / am pedalling* up and down tree-lined lanes.

Cycling in towns and cities, however, is another matter. Although some councils *spend / are spending* more money on constructing cycle lanes, cyclists in most towns and cities have to compete for space with lorries and buses. So when you cycle in the city, you *put / are putting* your life at risk.

2 Your secretary has left you written instructions for your forthcoming business trip to New York. Complete the note with an appropriate verb from the list in an appropriate tense. Where there are two possibilities, write both.

arrive	change	fly	fly back	leave	run	stay

You .... [1] from Heathrow Airport on BA flight 179. You .... [2] at JFK Airport at 20.00 (New York time). You .... [3] at the Hilton as requested.

The conference .... [4] for two days – the Saturday and Sunday, so you'll have Monday free. You .... [5] from JFK Airport on the Tuesday on BA flight 178.

By the way, I .... [6] your appointments for next Wednesday to the Friday, as I imagine you'll be a bit jet-lagged. I .... [7] a contact number with Ms Smith in case you need to contact me over the weekend.

Have a good trip!

3 Put the verb in brackets into the correct form, Present simple or Present continuous.

1 The average person .... (eat) about half a ton of food in a year. Many of us .... (consume) much more than we need.

2 Young people in particular have an unhealthy diet. They .... (eat) a lot of fast food like crisps and burgers, which .... (contain) a lot of fat.

3 The number of overweight people in the world .... (go up) dramatically. Being overweight considerably .... (increase) the risk of a heart attack.

4 The government .... (spend) more money than ever before on health education. Despite this, more people .... (take up) smoking than giving up.

5 At last, Andrew .... (follow) his doctor's advice on the need to take regular exercise. He now .... (go) swimming twice a week, he .... (cycle) to work every day, and he always .... (walk) upstairs instead of taking the lift.

2 Aspect

1 Match the sentence beginnings (1–6) with their endings (a–f).

1 ☐ She's having a shower
2 ☐ I've been out every night this week
3 ☐ I've taken an aspirin
4 ☐ She was cooking lunch
5 ☐ I'm putting on my shoes
6 ☐ I was eating an apple

a so I won't be very long.
b when I broke my tooth.
c so she can't come to the phone.
d when the electricity went off.
e so I'd like to stay in tonight.
f and I feel much better now.

2 Put the verb in brackets in the appropriate aspect (continuous or perfect) and tense.

1 I .... (start) doing exercise but I don't feel any healthier. I .... (eat) less so I must weigh less than I did a week ago.

2 I .... (read) the instruction manual but I still don't understand how it works. John .... (try) to explain it to me but I'm no wiser. Right now I .... (read) *An idiot's guide to the Internet* but I still haven't got beyond the first page.

3 Peter .... (lie) in bed with his right arm in plaster. He .... (cook) spaghetti bolognese, when he slipped on some tomato sauce. He can't do any more cooking for a few weeks!

3 Action verbs and state verbs

1 Choose the correct alternative, Present simple or Present continuous.

1 Alan: *I'm thinking/think* of taking up boxing. What *are you thinking/do you think*? Should I?
Paul: Are you serious? *Aren't you realizing/Don't you realize* how dangerous it is?
Alan: *I'm not agreeing/don't agree* with you at all. It's not any more dangerous than motor-racing.

2 Chris: *Are you seeing/do you see* Anna again?
Dave: Yes. Is that a problem?
Chris: It is actually. Pete *is believing/believes* he's still going out with her.
Dave: *I am seeing/see* what you mean.

3 Jane: What *are you doing/do you do*?
Kate: *I'm tasting/taste* the soup. It *is tasting/tastes* a bit salty. *I'm supposing/suppose* I'll have to add some water.

2 Complete the sentences with a verb from the list in the correct form, Present simple or Present continuous.

cost	do	have (×2)	help	know	own	prefer
smell	suppose	think (×2)	want	weigh		

1 Patrick .... a cottage on the west coast of Ireland. He .... to sell it because it .... a lot to maintain, but he .... it will be difficult to find a buyer because it's in such a remote spot.

2 'How much .... you .... John?'
'I've no idea. Eighty kilos? I .... not to know really.'

3 'What .... you ....?'
'I'm a counsellor. I .... people with their problems.'
'................... you .... a university degree?'
'Yes, but you don't need one.'

4 I .... this milk is all right. It .... a bit strange though. What .... you ....?

5 I .... a lot of problems with my car so I .... of getting a new one.

Writing

Making writing interesting (1): adjectives and adverbs

1 Read the text and answer the questions.

  1 Why was Susie Maroney's achievement so special?

    ....

    ....

  2 What do you think were the worst things she experienced?

    ....

    ....:..

2 The four verbs in italics in the article can be replaced by:
fed, dragged, stepped, smeared.
Match them with the verbs in the article. How do you think the new verbs improve the text?

3 The following adjectives and adverbs have been left out of the article. Match each word or phrase with the appropriate letter in the text.

  1 ☐ easy-to-digest
  2 ☐ favourite
  3 ☐ gingerly
  4 ☐ in her head
  5 ☐ much-needed
  6 ☐ occasional
  7 ☐ shark-infested
  8 ☐ shark-proof
  9 ☐ the exhausted but smiling

4 How do you think the adjectives and adverbs improve the text? Check your answers.

5 Imagine that you are Susie Maroney. You are going to write one or two paragraphs describing part of your swim. Use the following ideas and questions to help you.

  1 Choose **one** interesting moment. There are three suggestions in the box. First, think yourself into the situation by asking yourself questions, and make notes. Make sure your notes include descriptive words and phrases and not only facts. Adjectives and adverbs will make your description come to life.

Woman foils sharks in record swim to Florida

Australia's long-distance swimming champion, Susie Maroney, yesterday became the first person officially to swim unassisted across the 112-mile* a   Straits of Florida separating Cuba and the US mainland.

'I'm really happy about it,' said b   Miss Maroney as she *walked* c   ashore at Key West, where a crowd of 150 greeted her. Speaking with difficulty because her tongue was swollen from the long exposure to salt water, she described coming ashore as 'the best feeling in the whole world.'

Swimming in a 28ft-by-8ft† d   cage, and *covered* with Vaseline and suntan oil, the 22-year-old from Sydney overcame heavy seas to complete the distance in 24 hours 20 minutes – more than ten hours faster than had been expected.

Due to tides and a strong cross current, swimming the Florida Straits is regarded as about the most arduous endurance feat a swimmer can attempt. The unassisted, uninterrupted swim means that Miss Maroney could not sleep and was not allowed to touch the cage – floated by buoys and *pulled* by a support vessel – during the crossing.

'The hardest part was the night,' she said. 'It was so lonely. I was being stung by jellyfish. When I saw the sun in the morning, I was so happy another day was coming.'

She was permitted only an hourly break, treading water while being *given* high-protein and super-hydrating drinks, as well as e   spoonfuls of f   baby foods with yoghurt and chopped bananas.

Miss Maroney said she kept going by singing songs g   and remembering h   television shows. The family also gave her i   encouragement from the support boat and also in telephone calls relayed from Australia.

*180 kilometres   †8.5 metres by 2.4 metres

The Times

- **A shark attack**
  What did they look like? What did they do? How did you feel and react? What did the others do?

- **Twenty kilometres from Florida**
  How did you feel physically and mentally? Were you excited or just exhausted? Did you feel like giving up? What did you dream of doing when you arrived?

- **During the night**
  What could you see / feel? Was it quiet or was there some noise? What did you do? How did you feel at daybreak?

2 Organize your notes into one or two paragraphs. Remember to begin a new paragraph for a new topic.

3 Write out your notes into complete sentences. Then read through what you have written. Does your description sound interesting? Can the reader imagine they were there?

4 When you are satisfied with what you have written, write out your final version, correcting any mistakes in grammar, punctuation, and spelling.

2

Reading

Before you read

You are going to read part of a
short story. First, think of answers
to these questions.

1 Why do people go abroad to live?
Think of two or three reasons.

....
....

2 Why do some people want to go
back home again?

....
....

3 What problem(s) can stop people
returning home?

....
....

As you read

As you read the text for the first
time, answer questions 1–3 above
about Giorgiadis.

....
....
....

Glossary

insurmountable (line 3): that cannot be
    solved
Swahili (line 13): language used in trade and
    government in much of East Africa and Congo
kerosene (line 20): paraffin (kind of fuel
    made from coal or petrol)
like clockwork (line 28): without problems
in full working order (line 29): working
    perfectly
monopoly (line 31): exclusive right to
    supply or trade in particular goods or a
    particular service
seek one's fortune (line 36): try to find a
    way to become rich and successful
hand over fist (line 38): quickly and in large
    amounts
ouzo (line 41): strong, Greek alcoholic drink
    made from aniseed and drunk with water
sheer perversity (line 49): enjoyment from
    unreasonable behaviour

Sungura
by Tracey Lloyd

*After 40 years in a foreign country, the old man Giorgiadis
longed to return to the shores of his native Greece. But there
was one insurmountable problem …*

Giorgiadis watched the birds flying home across the bay, propped on
one elbow on his lumpy bed. Their flight across the bay, just a few
minutes before sunset, was an unchanging event by which he measured his
day, like the tolling of the cathedral bell. On the horizon the sun was
melting and dissolving like crimson paint in the watery blue of the lake.

Time to get up. Below in the bakery he heard the men loading the oven
with the first batch of evening bread. Sticky with heat and stiff with sleep he
lifted his heavy body off the bed and went down to the tap in the yard. The
delivery boy, Deogracias, was still asleep. Giorgiadis shouted at him in his
limited Swahili, while the tap water ran down his neck.

After 40 years of living in East Africa, Swahili was for him still no more
than a tool of his work, a blunt and imperfect tool, the language of
problems and profits. He could order flour and yeast and oil, he could shout
for the wood to be chopped and he could sell bread. But he still counted in
Greek. When he settled his bills or counted the loaves, the old Greek
numbers came back to him as easily as if he had never been away.

Wiping his hands on the seat of his trousers, he carefully lit the kerosene
lamp and stood it on the counter, unlocked the till, pushed the old cat off
his stool, and sat down to sell bread. This was the best time of the day –
there was a break in the endless traffic that ran along the shore road, and a
damp breeze which came off the sea. The shelves were heavy with sweet-
smelling bread and behind him in the bakery the sacks of flour, the rows of
empty tins, the pile of freshly chopped logs were waiting ready for the first
batch of loaves in the morning. He sighed with satisfaction – and regret.

The business ran like clockwork and Mohammed Said knew it. What a
fool Said was not to make him an offer. He could take it over in full working
order; he could install one of his sons behind the counter, and have a
monopoly on bread for the whole town. While he, Giorgiadis, could take his

Focus on vocabulary

1 Match the words (1–10) with their meanings (a–j).

1 ☐ long (line 2)
2 ☐ propped (line 4)
3 ☐ lumpy (line 5)
4 ☐ melt (line 8)
5 ☐ load (line 9)
6 ☐ yard (line 11)
7 ☐ wipe (line 20)
8 ☐ till (line 21)
9 ☐ stool (line 22)
10 ☐ shade (line 33)

a not smooth; containing hard or solid pieces
b fill to capacity with a particular thing
c drawer of a cash register in which money is kept
d seat with no back or arms
e (of a solid substance) become liquid
f want very, very much
g supported, often by leaning
h darker, cooler area out of the light and heat of the sun
i remove dirt, liquid, etc. by rubbing, e.g. with a cloth
j area outside a building, often with a stone or concrete floor

2 Check your answers. Then complete the sentences with one of the words above in an appropriate form.

1 The house has a small garden at the front and a .... at the back.
2 If you don't keep the butter in the fridge in summer, it ....
3 .... are less comfortable than chairs.
4 Could you .... the table? I've spilt some milk on it.
5 Make sure you keep stirring the sauce, otherwise it'll go ....
6 He left his bike .... up against the wall.
7 The cashier put the money in the .... and handed me my change.
8 I've been getting up early every day for months! I .... to have a lie-in.
9 At a bullfight the cheap seats are in the sun and the more expensive ones are in the ....
10 We .... the dishwasher and switched it on.

---

money and his tired old body back to Greece for a few last years of peace, to sit in the shade and sip some wine and talk with friends in the language of his youth. Nowadays, he even thought in Swahili, limited though it was. For what
35 was he to think about but the problems and profits that filled his days?

He had been a young man when he first left home to seek his fortune. There were plenty of Greeks in East Africa in those days, and news came back that they were all making money hand over fist. For Giorgiadis it came slowly, after years of hard work, but through it all he dreamt of Greece. As he sweated and
40 laboured to build up his business, he thought only of how he would sell it and return home, how he would buy a small café, drink ouzo with his patrons and live like a real Greek once more.

But there were problems in the new country, political unrest, changes of government – bad times to sell a business. It was always next year, next year he
45 would get away. And then suddenly he was an old man and Greece was still as far away as ever. And all because Said refused to buy. Said was his only hope – the one man in the town with the knowledge to run the business and the money to pay for it. But although he wanted the shop and recognised the old man's desperate need to sell, something, sheer perversity perhaps, made him refuse.
50 And instead of dreaming beneath the olive trees, Giorgiadis sat here, on a hard stool, and sold bread every morning and evening of his life.

Good Housekeeping

Comprehension

Are the following sentences True or False? Find evidence in the text to support your answers.

1 ☐ Giorgiadis had a sleep in the afternoon.
2 ☐ Giorgiadis was overweight.
3 ☐ Giorgiadis spoke Swahili fluently.
4 ☐ Giorgiadis's favourite time of day was the afternoon.
5 ☐ Giorgiadis's bakery was situated on a quiet road.
6 ☐ Mohammed Said owned the other bakery in the town.
7 ☐ Giorgiadis worked hard to build up the bakery.
8 ☐ Giorgiadis was one of the first Greeks to go to East Africa.
9 ☐ Giorgiadis had only decided to return to Greece fairly recently.
10 ☐ Giorgiadis would have lost money if he had sold his business before.

Understanding the text

1 What information in the text suggests that Giorgiadis's life was lonely, unhappy, and monotonous?

....
....

2 Giorgiadis's living quarters and bakery were quite basic. Find evidence to support this.

....
....

3 What is Giorgiadis's relationship with Mohammed Said?

....
....

4 Why do you think Mohammed Said will not buy Giorgiadis's bakery?

....
....

Vocabulary

Topic vocabulary: eating, drinking, talking

1 Complete the verb table below by matching the definitions (1–9) with the words in the lists. Use a dictionary if necessary. Which verb runs down the middle?

Eat	chew	gobble up/down	munch	nibble	swallow

Drink	knock back	sip	swallow

Talk	chat	discuss	gossip

Definitions

1 talk about a subject
2 drink sth in small amounts
3 break up food with the teeth
4 talk to sb in a friendly informal way
5 take small bites of sth; eat small amounts of food between meals
6 (informal) eat sth fast and in a greedy and noisy way
7 (informal) drink sth (especially an alcoholic drink) quickly
8 talk informally, especially about people's private affairs
9 eat (especially sth hard) noisily

2 Check your answers. Then complete the sentences with one of the verbs in an appropriate form.

1 If you don't .... your food properly, you can get indigestion.
2 I put on weight because I was constantly ....
3 Paul .... his beer and asked for another.
4 Sharon .... the coffee. It tasted very strong and she didn't really like it.
5 During the meal we .... about what we had been doing since we last met.
6 Nothing is a secret. People .... about you as soon as your back is turned.
7 He .... his way through four bags of crisps and a packet of biscuits.
8 We should .... this before we reach a decision.
9 Denise .... her sandwich in less than a minute.
10 He took the pills with a glass of water to help him .... them.

Phrasal verbs: get away, come off, take over

1 Match the phrasal verbs in the sentences (1–6) with their meanings (a–f).

1 ☐ It was always next year. Next year he would *get away*.
2 ☐ We're hoping to *get away* for a few days in September. We might go to Portugal.
3 ☐ A damp breeze *came off* the sea.
4 ☐ He took a huge risk investing all his money in the project but it *came off*. Now he's a millionaire.
5 ☐ He could *take over* the business in full working order.
6 ☐ Mr Smith will *take over* as managing director from next month.

a buy or gain control of a business
b escape
c assume responsibility for a job/task
d have a holiday
e be successful
f originate from a particular place or thing

2 Check your answers, then complete the sentences with one of the phrasal verbs in an appropriate form.

1 The prisoners .... as they were being escorted to the court-house.
2 It was a brilliant idea but, unfortunately, it ....
3 John drove most of the way but I .... for the last hour.
4 We didn't manage to .... last year, so this year we're going to go somewhere really exotic.
5 There are rumours that *American Express* .... the company next month in order to increase its share of the European market.
6 When he took the bread out of the oven, he could see steam .... the loaves.

3 Answer the questions.

1 Think of something you planned to do that did not *come off*.
2 When did you last *get away*?

Collocations: verb + noun

1 Match the nouns with the verbs below and write them in the space provided. Some nouns can go with more than one verb.

a business   a day off   a fool of oneself   a promise
a race   a record   fun of someone   turns

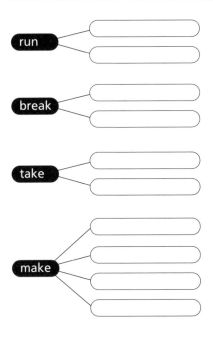

2 Check your answers, then answer the questions.

1 How do you feel if you make a fool of yourself?
....

2 What kind of person breaks promises? What is the opposite verb? ....

3 If you run a business, what is your position in the company? ....

4 Think of two ways in which you could make your fortune. ....

5 If you take turns with your partner or flatmate to cook the evening meal, how many times a week do you cook? ....

6 If you run a marathon, how far do you run? 15 kms, 26 kms, or 42 kms?
....

7 Do you make fun of people you like or people you dislike? ....

Grammar

1 Past simple and Past continuous review

Put the verb in brackets into the correct form, Past simple or Past continuous.

When I was seven years old, I .... **1** (play) a mean trick on my father. It was a Sunday afternoon and my father .... **2** (have) his afternoon nap on the sofa. My mother .... **3** (wash up) in the kitchen, and my sister, Susie, ... **4** (play) with her dolls upstairs. I .... **5** (be) bored.

Suddenly, I .... **6** (spot) my coloured pens, which .... **7** (lie) on the floor, and .... **8** (have) an idea. I .... **9** (decide) to colour in my father's bald patch in a variety of bright colours.

I should mention that my father is an extremely tall man, and that his bald patch is right in the centre of his head. For this reason nobody .... **10** (notice) anything strange until the next day when my father .... **11** (chair) an important business meeting. Every time he .... **12** (bend down) to look at his notes people .... **13** (laugh), and he couldn't understand why. It wasn't until the end of the meeting that someone .... **14** (point out) that he had a 'rainbow' on the top of his head.

My father was a very strict man with no sense of humour so you can imagine what .... **15** (happen) next. He .... **16** (throw away) my coloured pencils and .... **17** (cancel) my pocket money for a month. I never .... **18** (draw) again.

2 Past perfect

Complete the sentences with a verb from the list below in the Past perfect. You may need to use the negative form and change the order of the words.

drop	enjoy	go out	like	make	plan	rain
see	shine	stop	think	turn out		

1 It .... heavily all night and although it .... the ground was soaking wet.

2 We .... to go on a picnic but now we had to think of something else.

3 The sun .... every day for the previous fortnight and no one .... the weather would change so suddenly.

4 We couldn't go for a walk in the forest because the rain .... the paths so muddy that walking would have been difficult.

5 Dave suggested going to the beach but as the temperature .... no one fancied putting on their swimsuits. In the end we decided to go to the cinema. Nigel stayed in the apartment.

6 It was a bad decision. Julie .... already .... the film; she .... it the first time either.

7 The day was a disaster from start to finish. Nigel was cross because we .... without him; we .... the film. Nothing .... right.

3 used to, would

Decide whether it is possible to use both *used to* and *would* in these sentences. Cross out any wrong forms.

1 Life is quite different from what it *used to be / would be* like eighty years ago.

2 In the past, people *didn't use to have / wouldn't have* so much free time.

3 They *used to work / would work* a six-day week.

4 Sunday was their only day off, and on Sunday most people *used to go / would go* to church.

5 People *used to spend / would spend* their summer holiday in their own countries, if they could afford one. Nowadays the most popular holiday destinations are abroad.

6 Before the age of the aeroplane, if you wanted to travel to America from Europe it *used to take / would take* up to six weeks to get there.

7 The voyage *used to be / would be* hazardous, and some people never arrived.

8 In the past people *didn't use to live / wouldn't live* as long as they do now.

9 They *used to die / would die* at a much younger age – many from diseases like tuberculosis, which are now curable.

10 All in all, life *used to be / would be* much harder.

Past tenses

Decide which of the answers below (a, b, or c) best fills the gaps in the text. There are two correct answers for two of the gaps.

It wasn't the first time Emma ___1___ the law. When she was a child she ___2___ regularly but it ___3___ small things like sweets or chocolate.

Now, as she ___4___ the clothes, she ___5___ herself that it wasn't really a crime. It was a big store. They could afford it. She, on the other hand, was unemployed. The last time she ___6___ any new clothes was over a year ago.

It was strange that having decided to steal the skirt she ___7___ at all nervous, just excited. She ___8___. She couldn't see any security cameras and no one ___9___. Quickly, she ___10___ the skirt into her bag. It ___11___ easy. Maybe she should take a blouse to go with it.

She ___12___ her bag again when someone ___13___ her on the shoulder. 'Do you intend to pay for that?' the security guard ___14___.

	a	b	c
1	**a** broke	**b** had broken	**c** used to break
2	**a** used to steal	**b** would steal	**c** was stealing
3	**a** only used to be	**b** was only being	**c** had only been
4	**a** looked at	**b** would look at	**c** had looked at
5	**a** was convincing	**b** had convinced	**c** convinced
6	**a** used to have	**b** had had	**c** was having
7	**a** wasn't feeling	**b** didn't feel	**c** hadn't felt
8	**a** looked around	**b** was looking around	**c** would look
9	**a** was looking	**b** looked	**c** had looked
10	**a** was putting	**b** put	**c** used to put
11	**a** was being	**b** would be	**c** was
12	**a** just opened	**b** was just opening	**c** had just opened
13	**a** was tapping	**b** tapped	**c** would tap
14	**a** was asking	**b** would ask	**c** asked

Writing

Using correct punctuation

1 Read the story. Then match the names of the punctuation marks (a–j) with examples (1–10) in the text. Write the numbers in the boxes.

a ☐ apostrophe   f ☐ exclamation mark
b ☐ brackets   g ☐ full stop
c ☐ capital letter   h ☐ inverted commas
d ☐ colon   i ☐ question mark
e ☐ comma   j ☐ semi-colon

A Scotsman called **1**Robert Sinclair was going on holiday**2**. He lived in Glasgow and was going to visit his brother in Brighton for a short holiday.

If you wanted to be polite**3**, you would say that Robert Sinclair was **4**'careful' with his money. If you wanted to be impolite, you would say that he was mean. Certainly, it would be true to say that Robert didn**5**'t like spending money.

Now, Brighton is quite a long way from Glasgow, and Robert had to change stations when he arrived in London. Robert hadn't realized this until he got to Euston station**6**; he was at a loss what to do.

The connecting station, Victoria, was five kilometres away, and there were three alternatives**7**: walking **8**(a long way with his big, heavy cases); taking the Underground (a lot of stairs to climb); taking a taxi. The third option was the easiest. It was also the most expensive.

Robert decided to ask the price of the fare before making up his mind, and called over a taxi.

'How much is it to Victoria Station**9**?'

'Fifteen pounds,' said the driver.

Robert thought that was an awful lot of money and had almost resigned himself to walking when he had an idea.

'How much for the cases?'

'Oh, they go free,' answered the driver.

Robert's face lit up; his problem was solved. Smiling, he said to the driver, 'OK. Take these cases to Victoria Station and I'll see you there **10**!'

2 Check your answers, then use the examples in the text to help you match the punctuation marks with their main uses.

1 To separate two main clauses not joined by a conjunction. *semi-colon*

2 At the end of a sentence expressing a strong emotion. ....

3 To indicate the end of a sentence. ....

4 To enclose direct speech; to draw attention to a word which you are using with a special meaning. ....

5 To introduce a list of items; before a clause or phrase giving more information about the main clause. ....

6 To separate extra information or a comment from the rest of the text. ....

7 To separate words in a list; to separate phrases or clauses; before or after *he said*, etc. in direct speech; to separate long main clauses linked by a conjunction. ....

8 At the end of a direct question. ....

9 To indicate missing letters; to indicate that something belongs to someone. ....

10 At the beginning of a sentence or a name. ....

3 Read the short description of Josie's hospital experience. Then add the correct punctuation.

i remember it as if it were yesterday although it happened a long time ago when i was seven the doctor decided that my tonsils should be removed which meant a small operation and a short stay in hospital

my parents took me there in the afternoon and left me it was the first time i had been separated from my parents i was devastated i remember that for some reason my bed was in the centre of the ward so i felt that everyone was staring at me and cried myself to sleep that night

the next morning i woke up in a different bed next to an old lady my throat hurt and i didnt know where i was i remember a nurse saying im sure youd like some ice-cream wouldnt you its good for you i was not convinced and refused to eat it

that was my first time in hospital and the experience was so traumatic that i have had a horror of hospitals ever since just the smell of disinfectant is enough to bring it all back

4 Now write your own description. Either write about a time you spent in hospital as a patient or as a visitor, or write about your first time away from home.

1 Follow this plan.
  Paragraph 1   Say why you were in hospital/away from home.
  Paragraph 2 or 3   Describe one or two key events.
  Paragraph 3 or 4   Conclude your description with some appropriate concluding remarks.

2 Read through what you have written. Have you used correct punctuation? Check the grammar and spelling.

3 When you are satisfied with what you have written, write out your final version.

3

Reading

Before you read

1 Check you understand these words.

drought   famine   flood
global warming

2 How do you think global warming will affect the Mediterranean area by the year 2100? Choose the answer you think is correct.

1 Beaches will be smaller/bigger.
2 More/Fewer people will go to Mediterranean resorts on holiday.
3 Temperatures will rise by up to 4°/14°C.
4 There will be more/less rain in south-east Spain.
5 Sea levels will rise/fall.
6 Deserts will get bigger/smaller.
7 Southern Europe/North Africa will have water shortages.
8 Some Mediterranean countries will not be able to grow fruit/cereals.
9 Diseases like typhoid/malaria will increase.

As you read

Check your answers to **2** above.

Glossary

sink (headline): ruin
Greenpeace (line 13): an international organization which concerns itself with environmental issues
under threat (line 19): in danger
all the more reason (line 22): this makes it especially important
fossil fuels (line 24): fuel such as coal or oil formed from the decayed remains of plants or animals
climatologists (line 33): scientists who study climate change
livestock (line 67): animals such as sheep and cows kept on a farm
grazing land (line 69): land where grass is grown for feeding cattle

Could global warming sink your

Sea change: Flooding in Venice provided a premonition of what could happen to the city by 2100 if sea levels rise at their present rates

Climate change could ruin the appeal of Mediterranean resorts for holidaymakers. But if forecasts of famine, flood and
5 drought come true, a decline in tourism could be the least of the problems, says Nicholas Schoon, Environment Correspondent.

Shrinking beaches, and water
10 and food shortages could become the norm around the Mediterranean by as early as 2100, according to a Greenpeace report.

More than 100 million people
15 visit the sea's extensive, sunny coastline each year, and this had been projected to rise to as much as 340 million by 2025. 'Now this is under threat, as the possible
20 impacts of climate change are more fully realised,' says Greenpeace. All the more reason to reduce the world's rising consumption of fossil fuels, emissions
25 of which are changing the heat balance of the atmosphere.

The report is based on estimates for sea level and temperature rises made by the
30 UN's Intergovernmental Panel on Climate Change, which brings together most of the leading climatologists from around the world.
35 Temperatures are expected to rise by up to 4°C over many inland areas. Annual rainfall is projected to fall by 10–40% over much of Africa and south-eastern
40 Spain with smaller but significant changes elsewhere.

As oceans expand and glaciers melt in a warmer world, sea levels could rise by almost one metre by
45 the end of the century. Venice, the Nile Delta, and Thessaloniki in Greece could see sea level rises 50% higher because they are already sinking.
50 In Egypt it is estimated that a sea level rise of only 0.5 metres would displace 16% of the popula-

holiday plans?

tion if the coastline and riverbanks of the Nile Delta were not defended
55 against the rising sea. Much of the population lives on the low-lying delta. Beach resorts could lose much of their sand.

Deserts may spread northwards
60 and there will be a water shortage in countries like Egypt, Libya, Tunisia, Algeria, Morocco, and Syria, which already have only about 1,000 cubic metres a year or
65 less of water per person.

Crop production will be badly affected by droughts. Livestock production will also suffer because of a shortage of good grazing
70 land. One study predicts that large parts of Spain, southern Italy, and Greece could become unsuitable for cereal growing.

What is more, warmer condi-
75 tions are likely to increase the number of cases of tropical diseases like malaria and yellow fever.

The Independent

Understanding the text

1 Why might a decline in tourism be 'the least of the problems' for Mediterranean countries?

....

....

....

2 How does the text suggest the problem could be avoided? What could we do to improve the situation?

....

....

....

3 Which Mediterranean country could be worst affected overall? In what ways?

....

....

....

4 How reliable are the forecasts on climate change for the next hundred years?

....

....

....

Focus on vocabulary

1 Match the words from the article with their definitions.

1 ☐ appeal (line 2)   7 ☐ the norm (line 11)
2 ☐ resort (line 2)   8 ☐ project (line 17)
3 ☐ forecast (line 3)   9 ☐ impact (line 20)
4 ☐ decline (line 5)   10 ☐ estimate (line 28)
5 ☐ shrink (line 9)   11 ☐ sink (line 49)
6 ☐ shortage (line 10) 12 ☐ crop (line 66)

a situation where there is not enough of something
b amount of grain, fruit, etc. grown or collected in one season or year
c place where many people go on holiday
d judgement or calculation not necessarily detailed or accurate
e typical pattern
f process of becoming less in quantity, quality, or importance
g become smaller in size
h statement which predicts sth with the help of information
i calculate a change in, for example, size, amount, or cost of sth
j go down under the surface of sth
k attraction; interest
l strong impression or effect on sb or sth

2 Complete the sentences with one of the words above in an appropriate form.

1 Rice is the main .... in this area.
2 When you wash something woollen in hot water, it ....
3 I'm thinking of having my flat redecorated but I'm going to get an .... of the cost first.
4 Les Arcs is a popular ski .... in the French Alps.
5 The *Titanic* hit an iceberg and .... to the bottom of the sea.
6 Revenue from tourism is .... to total more than £3 billion.
7 The weather .... for tomorrow is good. It says it'll be sunny all day.
8 The new computer game soon lost its .... and the children went back to playing with their toys.
9 Her speech made a big .... on me. I became a member of Greenpeace not long afterwards.
10 A car used to be a luxury but now it is becoming .... for families to have more than one.
11 In times of war there is always a .... of fresh food.
12 There is a notable .... in the birthrate in most European countries.

Reference words

We use reference words to avoid repeating nouns or ideas.
Look back at the article and decide what the following reference words refer to.

1 this (line 16)   *the number of people visiting the Mediterranean*
2 which (line 25) ....
3 which (line 31) ....
4 they (line 48)   ....
5 their (line 58) ....

Vocabulary

Topic vocabulary: the environment

1 The words on the diagram are related to the environment. Use the clues below to help you fill in the missing letters.

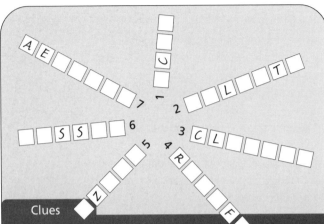

Clues

1 Rain which contains large amounts of harmful chemicals caused by the burning of coal and oil is called ... rain.
2 Make air, water, earth dirty and harmful to people, animals, and plants.
3 General weather conditions of a particular place.
4 A ... is a large area of trees in a tropical zone, such as the Amazon.
5 The ... layer is a layer of air high above the Earth which prevents harmful ultraviolet light from the sun from reaching the Earth.
6 Oil and coal are ... fuels.
7 An ... is a metal container in which liquids are kept under pressure and released in a spray.

2 Answer the question using the words in the list.

bottles	non-renewable resources	the environment
endangered species	rainforests	nuclear waste

Which of these can you:

1 cut down? ....
2 dump? ....
3 kill? ....
4 protect? ....
5 recycle? ....
6 use up? ....

3 Answer the quiz questions below.

QUIZ

1 Why are rainforests being cut down?
2 Name two endangered species.
3 Where is nuclear waste dumped? Why is this a concern?
4 Which sources of energy are non-renewable?
5 What other things can be recycled?

Phrasal verbs: *bring* + particle

1 Replace the verbs in italics in the sentences with *bring* in an appropriate form and one of the following particles: *about, down, in, out, together*. Use a dictionary if necessary.

1 The conference *united in one place* leading climatologists from all over the world. ....
2 The first electric car was *produced* in 1996. ....
3 Some people would argue that the government should raise the price of leaded petrol and *reduce* the price of unleaded petrol. ....
4 The smog in Singapore was *caused* by the burning of large areas of forest in Indonesia. ....
5 Governments around the world need to *introduce* tougher laws to regulate emissions from the burning of fossil fuels. ....

2 Check your answers. Then complete the sentences with *bring* in an appropriate form with an appropriate particle.

1 If they .... the cost of solar energy, maybe more people would change over to it.
2 The World Summit on the environment, which takes place every two years, ... all the world powers.
3 I've heard they .... yet another environmentally-friendly soap powder.
4 There are plans to .... legislation on the dumping of nuclear waste at sea.
5 The hole in the ozone layer .... changes in climate.

Word-building

1 Two of the most common noun suffixes in English are *-sion* and *-tion*. Complete the table with the missing verbs or nouns.

Verb	Noun
consume	consumption
....	emission
reduce	....
....	deterioration
predict	....

2 Check your answers. Then complete the sentences with an appropriate word from the table above in an appropriate form.

1 Previous .... by the Panel on Climate Change have come true.
2 As more and more people become vegetarian, the .... of meat and meat products has decreased.
3 Toxic gases are .... from car exhausts into the atmosphere.
4 In some parts of the country living standards are .... , not improving.
5 A .... in the consumption of fossil fuels is urgently needed.

Grammar

1 Futures review

will

Match the offers which Angela makes (a–h) with the situations (1–8).

1. [c] I don't know how I'm going to get to the airport.
2. [ ] I'll never get these letters typed in time.
3. [ ] Dinner will be ready in ten minutes.
4. [ ] Telephone!
5. [ ] Oh, no! My pen's run out!
6. [ ] I'm absolutely exhausted!
7. [ ] What shall we do about food for the party?
8. [ ] I wish I could swim.

a. OK. I'll answer it.
b. Sit down and I'll put the kettle on.
c. I'll give you a lift if you like.
d. I'll teach you.
e. I'll put the plates on the table.
f. I'll lend you one. Here you are.
g. I'll do some for you if you want.
h. I'll bring nuts and crisps.

will and going to

1. Choose the most appropriate form, *will* or *going to* for these predictions.

   1. I feel dizzy. I think I*'ll faint / 'm going to* faint.
   2. Let's start the meeting at 10 o'clock though I expect Michael *will be / is going to be* late as usual.
   3. Francis is stuck in a traffic jam. He*'ll miss / is going to miss* his plane.
   4. You can borrow Alan's book. I'm sure he *won't mind / isn't going to mind*.
   5. Look out! We*'ll crash / 're going to crash*!
   6. Don't do that! Lisa *will be / is going to be* very angry.
   7. Look at those clouds. It*'ll rain / 's going to rain*.
   8. Don't eat any more of that cake. You*'ll be / 're going to be* sick!
   9. John has just asked where the toilet is. I think he*'ll be / 's going to be* sick.
   10. In the future people *won't get married / aren't going to get married*. They *will just live / are just going to live* together.

2. Put the verb in brackets in the most appropriate form, *will* or *going to*.

   1. John: Have you made any New Year resolutions?
      Dave: Yes. I .... (give up) smoking; and I .... (get) fit. Have you?
      John: Yes. I've decided that I .... (not make) any New Year resolutions this year.
   2. When you arrive at the station a representative .... (meet) you. She .... (take) you to your hotel.
   3. Amy: .... you .... (see) Sean tomorrow?
      Sally: Yes. I .... (pass on) your message if you like.
   4. I know I .... (fail) my exams. I just haven't studied hard enough.

5. If all goes well, I .... (arrive) on time. Can you pick me up? If you can't, I .... (get) the bus.
6. 'We .... (have) a party next Saturday. Can you come?' 'Great! I .... (bring) some music.'
7. How old .... you .... (be) on your next birthday? I .... (be) thirty!
8. I expect John .... (come). He usually does.

2 Future continuous and Future perfect

1. Complete the dialogue with one of the verbs from the list in the Future continuous form.

dance	enjoy	lie	swim	travel	type	watch

   1. Emily: Just think, this time tomorrow I .... on a beautiful beach and you .... to work.
   2. In the afternoon I .... in the hotel pool and you .... letters.
   3. At 11 o'clock I .... at the best club in town and you .... something boring on television.
   4. Julia: I don't care! This time next month I .... myself in Florida and you'll have had your holiday!

2. Put the verb in brackets into an appropriate form of the Future perfect tense.

   1. A: .... you .... (finish) your essay by 6 o'clock?
      B: I expect I .... (write) most of it by then.
   2. A: Just think. By this time next week you .... (pass) your driving test.
      B: Well, I .... (take) it anyway.
   3. A: I'm sure Tim .... (not forget) it's your birthday today. He'll probably phone you later.
   4. Don't come at 6 o'clock. We'll still be eating. Come after 7. We .... (eat) by then.

3 Put the verb in brackets in the appropriate form, Future perfect or Future continuous.

2020 Visions

Here are the results of our survey into what you think life will be like in 2020. Most of you think that:

▶ We _____ (put) men on Mars.
▶ Society _____ (become) more caring.
▶ Medical science _____ (find) a cure for baldness.
▶ Most people _____ (walk around) with at least one artificial part in their bodies.
▶ Everyone _____ (use) plastic cards rather than cash.
▶ We _____ (discover) intelligent life elsewhere in the universe.
▶ Computers _____ (change) our lives completely.
▶ We _____ (pay) taxes for clean air just like we do for clean water.

Future forms

Put the verb in brackets in the appropriate form, *will*, *going to*, Future perfect, or Future continuous.

1 A: What .... you .... (do) with your free time now that you've retired?
   B: I think I .... (take up) a new hobby.
   A: .... you .... (come) down to the gym with me?
   B: No. I .... (not do) anything too energetic. Maybe I .... (take) swimming lessons.
   A: I .... (teach) you to swim if you like.
   B: How long .... it .... (take) me to learn?
   A: Not long. You .... (swim) like a fish in three months at most.
   B: All right. I .... (take up) your offer.
   A: I .... (send) you the bill. Just joking!

2 A: What .... we .... (do) this evening?
   B: Well I don't know about you but I .... (watch) TV. Brazil are playing Italy.
   A: Oh, no. Not football. I think I .... (go out).
   B: The match .... (finish) by 10. We could go out then.
   A: OK. But I .... (not watch) it.

3 A: .... you .... (do) all the housework by the time I get home from work?
   B: I .... (clean) the bathroom. I .... probably .... (make) the dinner at 6 o'clock. You .... (be) just in time to help me!

3 The language of contrast

1 Rewrite the sentences without changing their meaning. Use the words in bold.

1 Although people nowadays have more free time, they do not always spend it wisely.
   but *People nowadays have more free time but they do not always spend it wisely.*
   in spite of / despite ....
   however ....

2 They don't do anything useful with their time: they waste it.
   instead of ....

3 Some people believe that doing nothing is a sin. Others, however, believe that it is good for us to 'switch off'.
   whereas / while ....
   on the other hand ....

4 They believe that relaxation, not physical exercise, is the key to good health.
   rather than ....

5 'Switching off' is not easy. Actually, many people find it impossible.
   in fact ....

6 We may think that we are relaxed, but our muscles are tense and our brains still active.
   however ....
   although / even though ....

7 We should practise a form of meditation, like yoga, not watch so much television.
   instead of ....

2 Complete the text by adding one of the words or phrases from the list. Use each one only once.

although	but	even though	however	in fact
in spite of	instead of	not	rather than	

Some people would argue that .... [1] more relaxation, what we need is to be more active. And, ... [2] it is certainly true that too much stress can be bad for us, a certain amount of stress is necessary for our bodies to function properly. So, ... [3] taking early retirement, perhaps people should carry on working for longer.

.... [4] the fact that Alexander Brown is 80 years old, he still works. Ironically, he works for a charity called 'Age Concern', which looks after the interests of old people.

'I may be old myself .... [5] I'm still fit and healthy,' he said. Alexander recognizes the importance of keeping active, ... [6]. 'I walk everywhere .... [7] I've got arthritis. It is important that you fight old age, ... [8] give in to it. .... [9], that is the best piece of advice that I can give anyone.'

Writing

Topic sentences

When we write, we usually write in paragraphs. A paragraph usually expresses one main idea. This idea is typically introduced in the first sentence of the paragraph – the topic sentence – and elaborated in the remainder of the paragraph.

1 Read the travel article and the topic sentences 1–6 below, which have been removed from the text. Find four things you think attract tourists to Zanzibar.

....
....
....
....

2 Match the topic sentences (1–6) below with the paragraphs of the article (a–e). There is one extra topic sentence which you will not need.

1 The beach bungalows are simple but more than adequate.
2 The beaches are from your fantasies.
3 Few names conjure up such romance and mystery as that of Zanzibar, on the east coast of Africa.
4 Everyone is trying to sell you something.
5 The place is vibrant with ordinary day-to-day life.
6 The appeal of the place is actually in its scruffiness.

3 Underline the words and phrases which support the topic sentence in each paragraph.

4 Read the dictionary definitions.

> **maze** /meɪz/ *n* (usu *sing*) a network of paths or hedges designed as a PUZZLE in which one must find one's way

> **riot** /ˈraɪət/ *n* **1** a wild or violent protest by a crowd of people **2** ~ **of sth** a large or splendid display of sth

What do you think *a maze of streets* and *a riot of stalls* are? Use the dictionary definitions to help you.

ZANZIBAR

a
But what is it about Zanzibar that makes it seem so exotic to people who have never been there, and hardly know where it is?

b
Although there are a few smart hotels in the capital Stone Town, there are no magnificent buildings. Even the Catholic cathedral is drab, and the Portuguese fort, built in 1700, is run-down and shabby. But there is a delightful maze of scruffy streets full of tall buildings with massive ornate doors and plaster falling off the walls.

c
The narrow streets are full of local people buying their daily necessities in small, poky shops or from kiosks at the side of the road, which sell everything from cigarettes and fizzy-drinks to washing-up powder and tins of meat. There is the constant clatter of furniture being made, and along the sea-front a riot of stalls sell carvings of African tribesmen, animals, drums – all those things you instantly regret buying the moment you get home.

d
Palm trees fringe the golden sands and sway gently in the breeze. The roar of the waves mixes with the voices of the local women who chat and giggle as they walk along the shore collecting seaweed. An occasional fisherman strolls past carrying his catch in his hand.

e
Lighting comes from a storm lamp and a ceiling fan moves the warm air lazily around the room. Meals are served in a little restaurant nearby which serves freshly-caught fish and shellfish: tender octopus, big, tasty prawns, all washed down with a bottle of Sprite. Delicious. And all for just $16 a night.

The Independent

5 You are going to write a description of a holiday resort in your country or one that you have visited.

1 Continue the paragraphs below. Use the topic sentences given and the ideas in italics. Try to make your description as appealing as possible by including some descriptive adjectives and verbs.
   - The most popular resort in (*country*) is (*name*), and it is easy to see why.
     Describe the place: its location, buildings, streets, beach, etc.
   - (*Nationality*) food is well-known for its variety.
     Describe a typical restaurant and say what you can eat there.
   - (*Name*) has an agreeable climate which lends itself to many activities.
     Describe the weather and the activities you can do.

2 Read through your description, correcting any mistakes in grammar, spelling, and punctuation. Does your description make people want to visit the resort?

3 When you are satisfied with what you have written, write out your final version. Give it to someone to read and ask them what they think.

4

Reading

Before you read

1 Read this background information on the author of the story you are going to read.

> **Judah Waten (1911–1985) was born in Odessa in the Ukraine of Jewish parents. The family emigrated to Australia when the author was three years old. Although Waten's mother, a strict Jew, decided that she disliked Australia from the moment they arrived, they never returned to the Ukraine.**

2 Study the pictures. Make some predictions about the main characters in the story and their lives.

1 What were the writer's parents like?

....

2 Why was their home like this?

....

As you read

Check the predictions that you made.

Glossary

other-worldly (line 2): more concerned with spiritual than practical things
self-consciously (line 12): nervously, because you are worried what other people will think of you
deeds (line 15): intentional acts
pride oneself on (line 16): **take pride in** (line 23): be proud of
accumulated (line 31): increased in number
the old country (line 35): country of origin; where the person was born and brought up
Hebrew Bible (line 40): holy book of the Jewish religion
crestfallen (line 63): very sad because of unexpected disappointment

Mother

1   From my earliest memory of Mother it somehow seemed quite natural to think of her as apart and other-worldly and different, not of everyday things as father was. In those days he was a young-looking man who did not hesitate to make friends with children as soon as they were able to
5   talk to him and laugh at his stories. Mother was older than he was. She must have been a woman of nearly forty, but she seemed even older. She changed little for a long time, showing no signs of growing older at all until, towards the end of her life, she suddenly became an old lady.

2   I was always curious about Mother's age. She never had birthdays like
10   other people, and neither did anyone else in our family. No candles were ever lit or cakes baked or presents given in our house. To my friends in the street who boasted of their birthday parties I self-consciously repeated my Mother's words that such celebrations were foolish.

3   'As though life can be chopped into neat twelve-month parcels,' she
15   would say. 'It's deeds, not years, that matter.'

4   Although I often repeated her words and even prided myself on not having birthdays I could not stop myself from once asking Mother when she was born.

5   'I was born. I'm alive as you can see, so what more do you want to
20   know?' she replied, so sharply that I never asked about her age again.

6   In so many ways Mother was different. Whereas all the rest of the women I knew in the neighbouring houses and in other parts of the city took pride in their housewifely abilities, their odds and ends of new furniture, the neat appearance of their homes, Mother considered all these
25   things unimportant. Our house always looked as if we had just moved in or were about to move out. An impatient spirit lived within our walls; Father called it living on one leg like a bird.

7   Wherever we lived there were some cases partly unpacked, only some of the windows had curtains, there were never sufficient wardrobes so that
30   clothes hung on hooks behind doors. And all the time Mother's things accumulated. She never gave or threw anything away, no matter how old it was. A shabby green coat left to her by her mother hung on a nail in her

bedroom. Untidy heaps of tattered
books, newspapers and journals from
35 the old country decayed in corners of
rooms, while under her bed in tin
trunks she kept her dearest possessions.
In those trunks there were bundles of
old letters, two heavily underlined
40 books on nursing, an old Hebrew
Bible, three silver spoons given her by
an aunt with whom she had once lived,
a diploma on yellow parchment, and her
collection of favourite books.

8   From one of her trunks she would
frequently pick a book and read to my
sister and me. She never stopped to ask
us whether we understood what she
was reading; she said we would
50 understand later if not now. I liked to
hear Mother read, but she always
seemed to choose a time for reading
that clashed with something outside.
I would be playing football with the
55 boys in the street when Mother would
unexpectedly appear. Without even
glancing at my companions, she would
ask me to come into the house, saying
she wanted to read to me and my sister.
60 Sometimes I felt so humiliated that I
would remain where I was, my cheeks
burning, until she repeated her words.
Then, crestfallen, I would follow her into
the house.

From the short story *Mother*
by Judah Waten

Understanding the text

1 The writer's mother is described as 'other-worldly'. What evidence is there for this in the text?

....

2 Can you think of a possible reason why the writer's mother didn't want anyone to know her age?

....

3 'Father called it *living on one leg like a bird*.' What do you think this means?

....

4 What do we find out about the writer's mother from her possessions?

....

5 In what ways was the writer's childhood different from that of other children at that time? Do you think he minded this?

....

Focus on vocabulary

1 **Find a word or phrase in the text with the meanings below. The paragraph number is given in brackets.**

1 speak too proudly about something (2) ....

2 unwise; ridiculous; stupid (2) ....

3 tidy and ordered (3; 6) ....

4 severely; angrily (5) ....

5 small items of different types usually with little value (6) ....

6 old and in bad condition (7) ....

7 piles (7) ....

8 badly torn (7) ....

9 collection of things fastened together (7) ....

10 deeply ashamed (8) ....

2 **Check your answers. Then complete the sentences with a word you found in an appropriate form.**

1 Andy's dirty clothes lay in a .... on the floor.

2 I hate doing housework but I do it because I like everything to be .... and tidy.

3 Ever since Jack got promoted, he's never stopped .... about how much he earns.

4 Deciding to climb the mountain in such bad weather was an extremely .... thing to do. They could have been killed.

5 The tramp wore a .... black raincoat, which was tied around his waist with string.

6 'I've no idea where your pen is!' he answered ....

7 I keep a lot of .... in this box: buttons, foreign coins, stamps – things like that.

8 Inside the suitcase were .... of brand-new $100 bills.

9 I was so .... when I was caught cheating that I vowed never to do it again.

10 A dirty, ... flag, which must have been over a century old, hung from a pole above the door.

Vocabulary

Phrasal verbs: *go, give, throw, put, take, + away*

There are several phrasal verbs in English which are made up of a verb and the particle *away*. Each verb has two or more different meanings.

1 Read the sentences and match the verbs in italics with their meanings below.

1 ☐ We're *going away* for a few days at Easter. We need a break.

2 ☐ My headache *goes away* for a few hours but it always comes back.

3 ☐ She kept some of the money but *gave* the rest *away* to charity.

4 ☐ He refused to tell anyone his age, but he *gave* it *away* when he said he was 10 when President Kennedy was assassinated.

5 ☐ Don't *throw* those old magazines *away*. I'd like to read them.

6 ☐ He *threw away* his chances of promotion when he criticized the Managing Director to his face.

7 ☐ The children leave their toys all over the floor. I always end up *putting* them *away*.

8 ☐ He spends half of what he earns and *puts* the rest *away*.

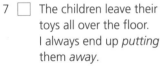

9 ☐ The rubbish is *taken away* three times a week.

10 ☐ Before he was put in prison they *took away* all his possessions.

a get rid of sth you do not want
b put sth tidily in its place
c leave home for a time, especially on holiday
d remove sth to another place
e accidentally reveal information
f disappear
g take sth from sb
h give without taking money in return
i save money
j lose an opportunity or waste a possibility

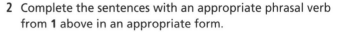

2 Complete the sentences with an appropriate phrasal verb from **1** above in an appropriate form.

1 My mother always told us that we should .... something .... for emergencies like unexpected house or car repairs.

2 We're .... in June this year rather than August. The weather isn't as hot then.

3 The teacher .... the magazine .... from the pupil, saying she could have it back later.

4 I'm always .... things .... without meaning to, so don't tell me any secrets.

5 Don't .... that .... If you don't want it, I'll have it.

6 If I had a million pounds, I .... some of it .... and spend the rest.

7 When we finished, the waiters .... our empty plates ....

8 The depression only lasts for a few days and then .... She soon feels better.

9 The politician almost .... a promising career when he admitted he hadn't been entirely truthful.

10 Stephen never .... his clothes .... He just drops them on the floor.

Topic vocabulary: ways of looking

In English there are several verbs which describe ways of looking.

1 Read the verb definitions (1–6) below. Then use sentences a–f to help you match the verbs in the list with their definitions.

gaze	glance	glimpse	peer	stare	watch

1 .... take a quick look at sth

2 .... look at sth with attention for a period of time

3 .... look at sb in a fixed way for a long time

4 .... get a quick look at sth or sb

5 .... look very closely at sth which is difficult to see

6 .... look for a long time at sth or sb especially in surprise or admiration or because you are thinking of sth else

a Sally *watched* her aerobics instructor do the exercise and then copied her.

b Jack *peered* through the fog trying to see where the road went.

c Don't you know that it's rude to *stare* at people like that?

d Lovers can spend hours just *gazing* into each other's eyes.

e I always *glance* at the headlines before turning to the back page.

f We *glimpsed* the cathedral through the train window.

2 Decide if the verbs in italics are correct. Correct any wrong verbs, making any other necessary changes.

1 John had lunch and then ~~stared at~~ *watched* the football match on television.
2 He *stared* at me for several minutes then said, 'Don't I know you?'
3 Amy *gazed* through the dirty windows to see whether anyone was inside.
4 I thought I *glimpsed* Toby as I was driving through town the other day.
5 Andrew *peers* out of the window for hours when he should be studying.
6 I *stared* the car drive slowly away.
7 Katy *glimpsed* quickly round the room to see if Stephen had arrived.

Word-building

The word *self-* can combine with other words to make new adjectives, nouns, and adverbs. For example: *I self-consciously repeated my mother's words.*

Complete the sentences with an appropriate *self-* word from the list. Use a dictionary to help you.

self-catering	self-centred	self-contained	self-defence
self-discipline	self-employed	self-service	

1 If you hate doing exercise, it requires a lot of .... to go to the gym regularly.

2 Kung-Fu, karate, and judo are all forms of ....

3 We decided to stay in a hotel instead of in a .... apartment.

4 He's totally .... He couldn't care less what the rest of us think.

5 I'd much rather be served by a waiter than eat in a .... restaurant.

6 Two-bedroom .... flat for rent in south London.

7 The main disadvantage of being .... is that there is no job security.

Grammar

1 Rules, needs, duties, and advice review

Complete the sentences with the most appropriate verb in the correct form: *must, have (got) to, need to, ought to, should, want to*. Sometimes more than one verb is possible.

1 I .... buy a new car but I can't afford it.
2 You .... tell Julie what Pat told you. I think she has a right to know.
3 I'm fed up. The boss says I .... finish these letters before I go home.
4 Thanks for the invitation but I'm too tired. I just .... go home and put my feet up.
5 Have you got a minute? I .... tell you who I saw with Malcolm last night.
6 You .... worry so much! I'm sure you'll pass your exam.
7 Some people .... take sleeping pills in order to get to sleep.
8 You really .... come on Saturday! It's going to be a great party.
9 Susan is a nurse. She often .... work at weekends.
10 What time .... you .... be at work?
11 I know I .... write to my parents more often than I do.
12 You .... sunbathe between 12 and 3. The sun is too strong.

2 Prohibition/no obligation

Choose the correct alternative in the sentences.

1 You *mustn't speak / needn't speak* during the examination.
2 You *mustn't come / don't have to come* if you don't want to.
3 I *didn't need to type / needn't have typed* the letters. Fran offered to do them for me so of course I accepted.
4 Now remember, Mrs Jones. You *mustn't take / don't have to take* more than three of these tablets a day. They're very strong.
5 I *didn't need to make / needn't have made* the sandwiches. Just after I'd finished Sue said that they had plenty.
6 I *didn't have to hurry / needn't have hurried*. When I got there the others still hadn't arrived.
7 Matthew *mustn't come / doesn't have to come* and pick you up. William can take you home.
8 He *didn't need to eat / needn't have eaten* when he got home. He was still full after such a good dinner.
9 You *mustn't swim / needn't swim* there. It's dangerous.
10 You *mustn't let me know / don't have to let me know* until Friday. That's early enough.

Mixed patterns

Answer the questions, using an appropriate verb.

1 What advice would you give someone who wants to learn English?

....

2 How many hours' sleep do you need a night?

....

3 Which activities are prohibited in public buildings and places, for example hospitals and buses, in your country?

....

4 If someone were coming to your country for a holiday in August, what clothes would you advise them to bring? What clothes wouldn't be necessary?

....

5 What rules are there where you study / work?

....

6 What activities are you obliged to do in your family, for example housework?

....

....

3 Speculating about past events

1 Speculate about the reasons for the appearance or behaviour of the people. Use *might have*.

1 Robert looks very pale. I wonder what's wrong?
(receive bad news; lose his job; sleep badly)

He might have received some bad news..............

....

....

2 Why didn't Daniella come to Joe's party?
(not invite; be ill; forget)

....

....

....

3 I'm sure I saw Susan driving Mandy's car.
(buy it from her; Mandy lend it to her; not be Susan)

....

....

....

2 Speculate about what happened in the situations below. Complete the sentences with *might / can't / must have*.

1 There was no answer when I called Jason at 10 o'clock last night.

a It's possible he was in the bath.

He might have been in the bath..............

b That's not possible. He was having a bath when I called him at 8 o'clock.

He can't have been in the bath..............

c He had probably gone to bed early. He said he was tired.

He must have gone to bed early..............

2 Tim promised to pick Sarah up at 6 p.m. but by 7.30 he still hadn't arrived.

a Maybe he forgot.

....

b That's impossible. He never forgets.

....

c I'm sure his boss asked him to work late.

....

3 What's wrong with Mandy? She's half asleep this morning.

a She probably went to bed late.

....

b That's not possible. She never goes to bed late.

....

c Maybe she didn't sleep well.

....

4 Joanne wasn't wearing her engagement ring when I saw her and she looked upset.

a Maybe she's lost it.

....

b There's only one reason I can think of. Her fiancé has probably broken off their engagement.

....

c It's not possible that she's finished with him. She's crazy about him.

....

Writing

Making writing interesting (2): adjectives, describing a person

1 Read the text. What is Nick's relationship with the writer and what does she like about him?

....

2 Complete the text with the correct missing adjectives. Use a dictionary if necessary.

ancient tweed	beautiful	blond curly	dark-blue woollen
high	long straight	old blue	piercing blue
thin-lipped and straight	untidy	worried	

Nick came round this evening.

'Are you busy? Can I come in?' he asked anxiously as I opened the door. I was pleased to see him and smiled into his **a** _____ eyes to reassure him.

'Hello. Come in, I was just going to open a tin of something – sardines or baked beans – which?'

He came in and sat down at the table, frowning as he tried to make a decision.

'Oh – sardines? Yes, sardines. Is that all right? Or would you prefer baked beans?'

'No, sardines are fine.'

Nick sat and watched me cut bread and open the tin. As usual he wore his **b** _____ jacket, bought a decade ago, **c** _____ jeans, and the **d** _____ sweater I had given him for his birthday. Nick is quite unable to cope with his appearance. He doesn't notice things, couldn't care less about what he wears, but worries because he knows that clothes matter to others. We often discuss the possibility of his buying a new jacket or pair of trousers. He asks my advice very seriously: where should he go, what colours should he buy, but we both know that he'll never get round to doing anything about it. He is actually perfectly happy with what he has, and when the jacket finally falls apart or the jeans go to holes, he will then drop into a local jumble sale and find replacements.

Nick certainly looks **e** _____ , but his face is quite **f** _____ . With his **g** _____ hair and his **h** _____ eyes he might have stepped out of a Renaissance painting. The **i** _____ nose and **j** _____ cheek-bones give him a heroic look. But his mouth is severe; **k** _____ . It surprises you with its hardness, and contradicts the gentleness suggested by the rest of his face. But the gentleness is there; it was what first attracted me to him. That and his ability to sit quietly and listen when I needed him to.

from Rainforest by Jenny Diski

Descriptive adjectives

Put the descriptive adjectives into the appropriate box. Two of the adjectives can go in more than one box.

crooked	full-lipped	generous	ginger	hazel	large
sad	shoulder-length	smiling	turned up	wavy	wide

Hair	Nose *large*	Mouth *generous*	Eyes

Order of adjectives

Put the adjectives in the sentences into the correct order. One sentence is already correct.

1 The girl had *ginger gorgeous shoulder-length* hair.
2 Peter has *brown wavy short* hair.
3 The woman had *hazel smiling* eyes.
4 The woman had a *large full-lipped* mouth.
5 She was wearing a *white cotton short* dress.
6 He had on a(n) *pink attractive new* shirt.

Describing character

1 When we describe a person we sometimes use adjectives to describe their character and frequently we suggest their personality through examples. Match the examples of behaviour in sentences 1–5 with the character adjectives a–e.

a selfish	b caring	c insecure	d clever	e affectionate

1 ☐ Patrick came top in every subject at school. Unlike the rest of us he never seemed to need to revise before exams.

2 ☐ Emma helped herself to the last piece of cake, saying 'No one else wanted any, did they?'

3 ☐ Whenever I had a problem he would find time to talk it over with me.

4 ☐ Mary never thought she was any good at anything. She would always ask, 'Are you sure it's all right?'

5 ☐ Every time I meet Alan he gives me a big hug and says how much he's missed me.

2 You are going to write a paragraph describing someone you know or an imaginary person.

1 Try to make your description as interesting as possible by using a variety of descriptive adjectives and giving examples of the person's behaviour. Take care to put your descriptive adjectives in the correct order.

2 When you have finished, read through your description. Correct any mistakes. Does your description sound interesting?

3 When you are satisfied with what you have written, write out your final version.

Reading

Before you read

How much do you know about denim jeans? Decide if the following statements are True or False.

1 ☐ The first jeans were made by a man called Levi Strauss.

2 ☐ Jeans were originally made for American cowboys.

3 ☐ The word 'denim' means blue.

4 ☐ Jeans became fashionable in the 1950s.

5 ☐ Most jeans are bought by young people.

6 ☐ The oldest pair of jeans is about 100 years old.

As you read

Check your answers. Correct any wrong statements.

Glossary

badge of rebellion (line 2): something which shows that the person resists authority and control

fall victim [to sth] (line 16): be damaged because of sth

worst possible fate (line 17): worst thing that could possibly happen

gold prospectors (line 20): people who look for gold

sailcloth (line 21): strong, rough cloth used for making sails

serge de Nimes (line 21): a kind of cloth from the French town of Nimes

Rebel Without a Cause [1955] (line 25): film in which James Dean played the part of a teenage rebel

decadence (line 27): state of low standards in social and moral behaviour

cool (line 33): fashionable

out (line 34): unfashionable

Death

1 Blue jeans were once the badge of rebellion. Now the image is rapidly fading, says **ANNA PUKAS**

2 They are an essential item in every wardrobe. Jeans – practical, hardwearing, timeless and classless – are worn by everyone from the humblest worker to the American president.

3 But these are tough times for the denim industry. 43 million people have bought jeans this year. a _____. But 43 million is 10% fewer than last year – and the lowest number for a decade. Levi Strauss has been forced to lay off 1,000 workers because of falling sales. And the VF Corporation, which makes Lee and Wrangler jeans, is planning to cut its 65,000 workforce by 2,000 over the next four years.

4 b _____. It seems that jeans have fallen victim to the worst possible fate for a fashion item; they have become respectable. And respectable means middle-aged, sensible, and *boring*.

5 c _____. The first pairs were made in the 1850s for San Francisco gold prospectors by Levi Strauss, a Bavarian immigrant. He used a hardwearing sailcloth from France known as 'serge de Nimes' – hence *denim*.

6 For 100 years only cowboys and prisoners wore them until Hollywood adopted them and they became fashionable overnight. A generation of young men yearned to be 'rebels without a cause' like the film star James Dean. d _____.

7 In Communist countries jeans meant Western decadence, and during the Sixties, they were even banned in East Germany. e _____. The teenagers of the Fifties are now grandparents; those of the Sixties are middle-aged. But they're still wearing jeans.

8 In recent years the highest proportion of sales have been to the 45–54 age group. Sales to young people are falling. Wearing jeans is no longer 'cool'. Sandie James, fashion editor of *Youth Style* magazine explains: 'Denim is out. It just isn't as popular with young people any more.' f _____. And while actresses like Goldie Hawn may look fantastic at 50 in skin-tight denims, that isn't the point. The point is that she is 50 and no 20-year-old wants to dress like her mother.

9 So, having enjoyed unique status for nearly 40 years, jeans now seem destined for the museum. Ancient pairs sell at auction for thousands of dollars. In March Levi Strauss paid over $30,000 for a 100-year-old pair found in an old mine in Colorado. They are believed to be the oldest in existence. g _____. Does this mark the beginning of the end for denim?

The Express

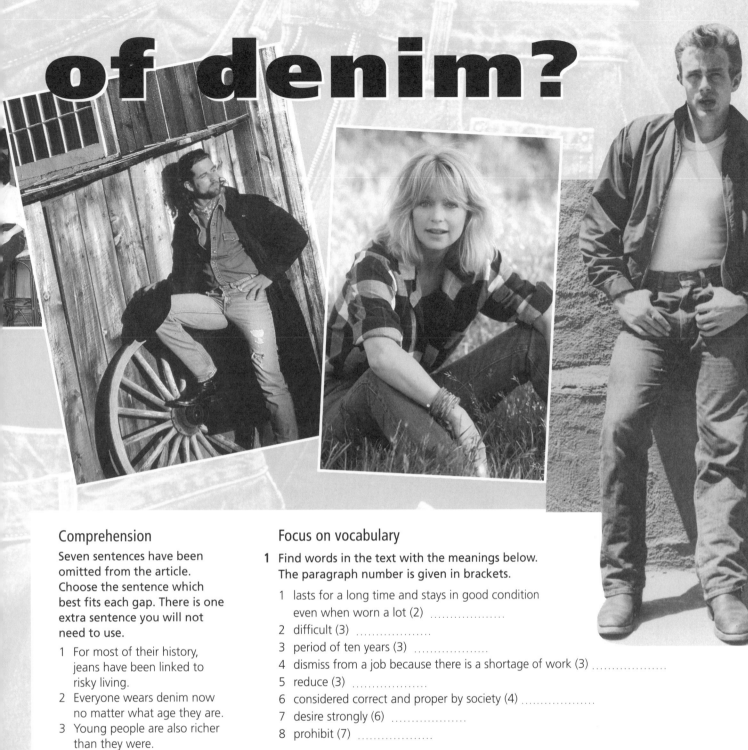

# of denim?

Comprehension

Seven sentences have been omitted from the article. Choose the sentence which best fits each gap. There is one extra sentence you will not need to use.

1 For most of their history, jeans have been linked to risky living.
2 Everyone wears denim now no matter what age they are.
3 Young people are also richer than they were.
4 So what exactly is the problem?
5 But it is a bad sign when jeans makers start buying their own products back.
6 But time passes.
7 On paper, these sales figures still sound good.
8 Teenage girls wore theirs with knotted blouses to look like that popular actress of the time, Brigitte Bardot.

Focus on vocabulary

1 Find words in the text with the meanings below. The paragraph number is given in brackets.

1 lasts for a long time and stays in good condition even when worn a lot (2) ....
2 difficult (3) ....
3 period of ten years (3) ....
4 dismiss from a job because there is a shortage of work (3) ....
5 reduce (3) ....
6 considered correct and proper by society (4) ....
7 desire strongly (6) ....
8 prohibit (7) ....

2 Complete the sentences with one of the words you found in an appropriate form.

1 Our family has lived in this house for three ....
2 We've had to take some .... decisions recently.
3 He was fined £500 and .... from driving for two years.
4 The government plans .... class sizes from 35 to 30 in the next two years.
5 After 40 years in Africa, the old man .... to return to his native Greece.
6 We had thought that they were a .... married couple and were shocked when the police arrested them for fraud.
7 Last year the company .... ten per cent of its workforce.
8 The carpet used in airport terminals has to be .... because so many people walk on it.

Vocabulary

Topic vocabulary: employment

1 Complete the table.

Verb	Noun	
promote	*	
employ	*	(general noun)
	....	(person who employs others)
	....	(person who is employed)
retire	....	
resign	*	
apply	*	(general noun)
	....	(person who applies)

2 Mark the stress on all the words. Here are some clues to help you.

- All the verbs are stressed on the same syllable.
- Four of the nouns have the stress on the same syllable as the verb.

3 Check your answers to **1** and **2**. Which verbs collocate with the nouns marked *? Complete the sentences with one of the verbs below in an appropriate form.

get   send off   hand in   look for

1 After working in the company for several years David finally .... the promotion he deserved.
2 Adrian .... employment for over six months now.
3 Ruth .... applications for ten jobs but she hasn't received any replies yet.
4 I've decided that I don't want to work here any longer. I .... my resignation first thing tomorrow.

4 Fill in the missing letters to give the words which have the same meaning as the definitions.

1 p☐r☐-t☐☐e   working for only part of the day or part of the week
2 f☐☐☐-t☐☐☐   working all day, five or six days a week
3 t☐☐d☐ u☐☐on   an organization formed to protect the rights of employees
4 go on ☐t☐☐k☐   refuse to work in order to try to get more pay, better working conditions, etc.
5 s☐☐k; f☐r☐   (two verbs) order an employee to leave their job (informal)
6 make someone r☐d☐☐d☐☐t   dismiss someone from work for economic reasons

5 Complete the texts with an appropriate word or words from exercises **1–4** above.

Andrew was .... [1] last year when overseas sales in the company he worked for dropped. Andrew has .... [2] for several jobs but has not had any success so far. Times are hard. Although his wife works, it is only a .... [3] job and is badly-paid.

Employees at XYZ Mechanics .... [4] yesterday when plans to cut jobs were revealed. Representatives of the .... [5] will meet management later today for talks.

Phrasal verbs: get + particle

1 The most common phrasal verb combination in English is *get* + particle. What do you think the phrasal verbs below mean? Use the example sentences 1–8 and your dictionary to help you.

1 It has taken her a long time to *get over* the accident.
....
2 He always finds some excuse for *getting out of* doing the washing-up. ....
3 I finally *got round to* cleaning out that cupboard last week. ....
4 While we watched the match we *got through* two large bottles of coke, two hamburgers each, and a large packet of crisps. ....
5 This endless rain is really *getting* me *down*. I need a holiday somewhere sunny. ....
6 I couldn't have *got by* without your help. ....
7 Dad never let me stay out late but Susie always managed to *get round* him. She was his favourite. ....
8 He is a good public speaker. He has no problem *getting* his message *across*. ....

2 Check your answers. Then complete the sentences with *get* in an appropriate form with an appropriate particle.

1 I never .... seeing Spielberg's last film. I was always too busy.
2 She is slowly .... her illness.
3 It doesn't matter how many times you ask, the answer is still no. You won't .... me.
4 A successful advertisement .... its message .... in one powerful image or a few words.
5 Steve hasn't had a job for over a year. It's beginning to .... him ....
6 I .... washing the dishes by pretending I was ill.
7 We went for a lovely Indonesian meal last night. There were fifteen courses. We only managed to .... ten.
8 During the war people managed to .... on very little.

Grammar

1 Conditionals review

Read what the people have to say about the following topics.
Put the verb in brackets into an appropriate conditional form.

The lottery

1 I hardly ever buy a lottery ticket. I don't know what I .... (do)
  if I .... (win).

2 I've got one for tonight's lottery. If I .... (win) this time, it
  .... (solve) all my problems.

3 I changed my lottery numbers last week. If I .... (keep) the
  original numbers, I .... (win) half a million pounds!

4 I don't buy a lottery ticket regularly but if I .... (remember),
  I usually .... (buy) one.

Holidays

1 I usually stay at home but if I .... (go away), I generally
  .... (go) to my sister's for a few days.

2 I'd love to go to Florida. If I .... (have) enough money,
  I .... (spend) a month there.

3 I was going to go to Australia but I broke my leg so I couldn't go. If
  I .... (not break) my leg, I .... (go) to see my sister
  in Sydney.

4 I'm not absolutely sure yet but I .... probably ....
  (go) skiing if there .... (be) enough snow.

Relationships

1 If I .... (not go) to the dance, I .... (not meet)
  my wife!

2 If you .... (meet) someone you get on with, it ....
  (be) the most wonderful thing in the world.

3 I can't imagine myself getting married at all to be honest. But certainly,
  I .... never .... (get married) in a church.

4 If you .... (not go out), you .... (not meet) anyone,
  will you?

Work

1 It's a bit too late to do anything about it now. If I .... (have)
  the money when I was younger, I .... (set up) my own
  business.

2 You .... (get) a lot of satisfaction if you .... (work)
  in a job that you enjoy.

3 I only applied because my mum said I should. If she .... (not
  insist), I .... (not apply).

4 I'm going for an interview tomorrow. If I .... (get) the job,
  I .... (be) really pleased.

2 The verb *wish*

Put the verb in brackets into an appropriate form.

1 I'm really tired. I wish I .... (not go) to bed so late.

2 I hate Mondays. I wish I .... (not have to) go to work.

3 I wish you .... (stop) making that awful noise. I can't concentrate!

4 Have you seen Damon's new car? I wish I .... (can) afford a BMW.

5 I wish we .... (able to) go but it was just impossible.

6 I wish I .... (be) as thin as you. I wish I .... (not have to) watch what I eat.

7 I wish you .... (not keep) interrupting me. I'll never get this finished.

8 When the weather's like this I wish I .... (live) in California.

9 I wish I .... (tell) you. I'm sorry I didn't.

10 I wish you .... (tell) me when you're going to be late. It's easy enough to pick up the phone.

3 Mixed conditional sentences

Read the short text below about two people who won the lottery but wish they hadn't. Then complete the sentences with an appropriate conditional form.

BOB BRONSON and PAUL McNABB each won $1 million in a lottery 20 years ago. Sadly, their good fortune created more of a nightmare than a dream come true.

■ BOTH their homes were burgled soon after they won.

■ BRONSON and his wife moved to Texas after their home had been broken into on numerous occasions.

■ BRONSON invested his money badly and lost everything. He is now broke.

■ NOW he and his wife both clean toilets. Bronson had to take a second job to pay the bills. He packs water-melons.

■ McNABB got so fed up with all the letters asking him for money that he left his home state of Maryland.

■ IT DIDN'T take him long to spend his money either. These days he earns his living driving a cab in Las Vegas, where he now lives.

---

1 If they *hadn't won* the lottery, their homes *wouldn't have been burgled.*

2 If the Bronsons' house .... so many times, they .... to Texas.

3 If Bronson .... his money badly he .... everything.

4 If he .... everything, he .... broke now and he .... toilets.

5 If he .... to take a second job, he .... water-melons now.

6 McNabb .... Maryland if he .... so fed up with all the letters asking him for money.

7 If he .... his money so quickly, he .... a cab in Las Vegas.

4 Past verbs with present or future meaning

It's time

Write sentences using *it's time you/he*, etc.

1 Alan's shoes are so old they're falling to pieces.
It's time Alan bought some new shoes.

2 He ought to start looking for another job. He hasn't had a job since he was made redundant four years ago.

....

3 John's hair is very long. He looks awful!

....

4 Julie really needs a holiday. She'll make herself ill otherwise.

....

5 If you don't want to be late, you'd better get up.

....

I'd rather

Rewrite the second sentence in the dialogues using *I'd rather*. You may need to use the negative form.

1 'Could I start work half an hour late tomorrow?'
'Could you come in on time?'
I'd rather you came in on time.

2 'Do you want me to finish these letters now?'
'Could you do this photocopying instead?'

....

3 'Shall we postpone the meeting?'
'No, that's not a good idea.'

....

4 'Is it OK if I ask Ann to send this fax?'
'No. Can you send it yourself, please?'

....

5 'Can I tell Paul?'
'It would be better not to tell him.'

....

Writing

Connecting ideas (1)

1 Read the short description of the two people in the photograph. What do they have in common? In what ways are they different?

You would expect James and Scott to have a lot in common. They are, after all, identical twins. Both are tall, blond, and blue-eyed, and it is difficult for strangers to tell them apart. **But** even identical twins have their own individual personalities.

James was the first-born. He arrived a full thirty minutes before his twin brother and, possibly because of this, he took on the role of protective elder brother from an early age.

When they were at school, **for instance**, James would frequently get into fights on his brother's behalf. Scott hated violence in any form and, because he refused to fight the other boys, they constantly insulted and provoked him. James, **by contrast**, actually quite enjoyed physical contact. **Besides**, because he was taller and stronger than most of the other boys, he usually came off best in any fight.

James and Scott get on extremely well. They share a lot of interests – they both like sailing and fishing – and there is a closeness between them that is not generally found between brothers and sisters who are not twins. **On the whole**, they enjoy being twins. **However**, they dislike it when people confuse them and treat them as if they were two halves of one person.

2 Which words and phrases in **bold** in the text are used to:

> introduce a contrast:

> give additional information:

> introduce an example:

> make a generalization:

Write these words and phrases in the appropriate box above.

3 Add the words and phrases below to the boxes in **2**. (There are more examples of the language of contrast on page 22).

apart from	as well as	by and large	on the other hand
in comparison	in general	on the one hand	for example

4 Complete the sentences with an appropriate word or phrase from the boxes.

1 My mother is seven years older than my father .... you would think she was younger than him.

2 Her hair is still the same coppery-red colour it was when she was young. .... my father's is grey and receding.

3 .... a mutual interest in my brother and me, they have nothing in common.

4 .... doing all the housework, my mother also has a full-time job.

5 .... , my parents get on well. They seem to agree on most things.

6 One thing they do argue about, ... , is where to spend our annual summer holiday.

7 My mother likes to do something different every year – .... last year we went on a camping holiday in Sardinia.

8 My father is difficult. .... he likes to go abroad but .... he doesn't like hot weather.

5 You are going to write a short description of two people you know who either get on well or don't get on at all. They could be brother and sister, boyfriend and girlfriend, husband and wife, or teacher and student.

1 Make some notes about what they have in common and in what ways they are different. Think about:
   - their physical appearance
   - their character
   - their habits
   - their likes and dislikes.

2 Write out your notes into paragraphs using appropriate words and phrases to connect your ideas.

3 Read through your description, correcting any mistakes in spelling, grammar, and punctuation you find. Does your description sound interesting? Are your ideas introduced in an appropriate way?

4 When you are satisfied with what you have written, write out your final version.

6

Reading

Before you read

You are going to read an article about the age at which people in different jobs *reach their peak* (perform at their best).

Decide whether you think the following statements are True or False.

1. ☐ Female swimmers are at their peak when they are in their teens.
2. ☐ Mathematicians do their best work in their thirties.
3. ☐ Novelists reach their peak when they are older.
4. ☐ Oil rig divers are usually young.
5. ☐ Goalkeepers can peak at a later age than other footballers.
6. ☐ 100 and 200 metre runners reach their peak at an earlier age than long-distance runners.

As you read

Check your answers. Correct any wrong statements.

Glossary

hit (headline): reach (a particular level)
catwalk (line 8): platform along which models walk in a fashion show
rule of thumb (line 28): practical and approximate way of measuring something
gauge (line 29): calculate
to say nothing of ... (line 36): this expression gives more force to the point you are making
oil rig (line 64): large structure with equipment for extracting oil, especially from under the sea
mainstream sports (line 72): most popular sports
has-been starlet (line 101): young actress famous in the past but not any longer
mega-stardom (line 102): status of being an extremely famous actor, performer, etc.

When you hit your career peak

1 'It's often assumed that youth is a bonus in most professions. But frequently, it is only when you have a combination of both age and experience that a person can truly be said to be at their peak.'

2 By the age of 26 most top catwalk models are thinking of retirement or at least a change of career. They have seen it all and done it all. Maybe they are wise to quit when they are at the top, and before time blemishes that perfect image.

3 Twenty-six is a bit young to be at the peak of your career but then that's the nature of the modelling business. Other professional peaks vary hugely, depending on any number of factors.

4 The great soprano Dame Joan Sutherland, for example, was widely considered to be at the height of her powers at the age of 33, whereas female swimmers are regarded as old when they're out of their teens.

5 There are no exact rules of thumb but it is possible to gauge when you are likely to be at your best, depending on the kind of job you do.

6 Great mathematicians will do their best work in their early twenties, while novelists will have to cram in years of experience, to say nothing of perfecting their style of writing, before they can truly be at the summit of their career.

7 'It's often assumed that youth is a bonus,' says Graham Pitts, of the employment specialist group *Focus*. 'But frequently it is only when you have a combination of age and experience that an individual is truly able to peak in their career.

8 'People who work in television programming, for example, tend to be young because they need to be both creative and able to work under extreme pressure.

9 'However, a judge would not only need some experience of life in order to be able to do his job but also an in-depth understanding of the legal process, which a young man or woman would simply not have, no matter how talented they were.'

10 On the whole, physical professions tend to be geared more towards the young. However, oil rig divers, surprisingly, peak much later at around 43. Hamish Peterson, managing director of KD Marine in Aberdeen, says statistics prove divers are getting older. 'They can still dive in their fifties with no adverse effects,' he says.

11 Even within the field of main-

Understanding the text

1 The verb 'blemish' means to spoil the appearance of something that is beautiful or perfect. How can time 'blemish' a perfect image?

....

2 Why has the writer included so many quotations in her article?

....

3 Why do you think goalkeepers can peak a bit later than other footballers?

....

4 There are four adverbs in the article which tell us the writer's attitude to what she is writing. For example, *maybe* (line 11) tells us that the writer is not sure whether models should quit when they are at the top. Find three more 'attitude' adverbs in paragraphs 10 and 13. What do they tell us about the writer's attitude in each case?

....

Focus on vocabulary

1 Find four different phrases in paragraphs 4, 6, 11 and 12 with the same meaning as 'at the peak'.

....

2 Find a word or phrase in the article with the meanings below. The paragraph number is given in brackets.

1 accept something as true without question or proof (1) ....

2 pleasant extra which wasn't expected (1) ....

3 stop doing sth; leave a job or career (2) ....

4 do or learn a lot in a short time (6) ....

5 perform a lot of tasks and take a lot of decisions without having sufficient time (8) ....

6 thorough and detailed (9) ....

7 be designed for a particular group or activity (10) ....

8 harmful; bad (10) ....

9 complain about sth (13) ....

3 Check your answers. Then complete the sentences with an appropriate word or phrase.

1 Angie's going to .... teaching and go into business.

2 The plane was delayed because of .... weather conditions.

3 I .... Ross is coming but I haven't actually asked him.

4 We were only in Sydney for two days but we managed to .... in a lot of sights.

5 Some people are never happy. They'll always find something to .... about.

6 People who .... in their jobs will often suffer from stress.

7 The results are based on an .... analysis of the data collected.

8 A lot of pop music nowadays .... very young teenagers.

9 They were happy that it didn't rain, and the brilliant sunshine was a real ....

stream sports, peak ages can vary widely, according to Ian Hodge, a
75 sports statistician. 'Footballers tend to be at their best in their mid-twenties, except for goalkeepers, who can peak a bit later,' he says.

12 And runners peak at differ-
80 ent times, according to Hodge. 'A long distance road runner will probably be at the top in his thirties,' he says. 'That is because three or four hours running every
85 day is not socially the right thing for someone younger to do. Long-distance running requires the kind of dedication which most young people just don't have. But
90 sprinters – 100 and 200 metre runners – can make the most of their talent right from the start, which means they tend to peak when they are teenagers.'

13 Fortunately, however, there are exceptions to the rule in every profession. Actresses are always moaning about the fact that there are no good roles for them after
100 the age of 40, but look at Joan Collins, who leapt from has-been starlet to mega-stardom in her fifties, or Mary Wesley, who published her first novel when she
105 was in her seventies. Thankfully, it seems you are never too old to do what you really want.

The Daily Express

Vocabulary

Word-building

1 Complete the table by adding the missing noun or verb.

Verb	Noun
combine	combination
....	experience
perfect	....
prove	....
require	....
....	dedication
vary	....
	....

2 Mark the stress on the words as in the example. Remember that prefixes are not usually stressed. Check your answers.

3 Complete the sentences with an appropriate word from the table in an appropriate form.

1 One of the .... of the job is that you work Sundays.

2 In winter, temperatures can .... by as much as 10 degrees. In summer the .... is less noticeable.

3 Michael has that rare .... of good looks and modesty.

4 Although the police suspect he is the killer, they have no .... If they can't .... that he did it, they'll have to release him.

5 Hydrogen .... with oxygen to form water.

6 You are .... to show your passport when you enter the country.

7 We have .... a lot of problems with the new computer.

8 The food is good but as there isn't a lot of .... it gets rather boring.

9 Many novelists .... their work to their families. The .... is usually written on the first page.

10 He spends hours practising to .... his technique. He is aiming at absolute ....

11 Janet was offered the job although she had no .... of hotel work.

Topic vocabulary: stages of life

1 Use the definitions and clues below to help you find the fourteen missing words in the wordsearch. Words can run forwards, diagonally, up, or down.

Wordsearch

T	A	D	O	L	E	S	C	E	N	C	E
O	E	Q	R	S	D	P	E	P	A	T	L
D	P	E	N	S	I	O	N	R	R	V	D
D	R	M	O	L	M	T	B	E	E	C	E
L	O	A	D	R	O	S	A	G	T	U	R
E	M	R	P	L	A	G	Y	N	I	L	L
R	O	R	L	A	T	E	E	A	R	L	Y
Z	T	I	X	L	K	G	I	N	E	T	R
F	I	A	T	E	E	N	S	T	M	O	S
R	O	G	A	L	T	O	U	T	E	R	T
D	N	E	F	I	G	S	U	H	N	I	P
A	R	D	I	V	O	R	C	E	T	A	M

Definitions

1 a better job in the same company

2 formal agreement between a man and a woman which makes them husband and wife

3 if you are 28 or 29 you are in your __ twenties

4 if you are 31 or 32 you are in your __ thirties

5 if you are 44, 45 or 46 you are in your __ forties

6 if you are 13 to 18 you are in your __

7 if you are expecting a baby you are __

8 a polite adjective which means old

9 period when you stop work because you have reached a particular age

10 child who has only recently learnt to walk

11 period of time when one develops from a child into an adult

12 another name for pimples

13 money paid regularly by the government or a company to people above a certain age

14 legal agreement which ends a marriage

2 Check your answers. Then complete the sentences with one of the words from the wordsearch in an appropriate form.

1 For many years in Britain the .... age was 65 for men and 60 for women.

2 Bill has worked for the company for 15 years but only recently got the .... he deserves.

3 Jason's wife, Ruth, is six months' .... It'll be their first child.

4 The .... of David Jones and Emily Foster will take place at St Thomas' Church on Saturday 4 July.

5 After he retired, he was pleased he had paid into a .... scheme.

6 In Britain, the .... rate is going up as more and more marriages break down.

7 .... is a difficult time for teenagers and their parents.

Phrasal verbs:
bring up, make up, take up, break down

1 Match the phrasal verbs with their meanings. Use a dictionary if necessary. Each verb has two different meanings.

---

bring up   break down   make up   take up

---

1 collapse in tears

....

2 introduce a subject into the conversation

....

3 start a new job or activity

....

4 (of a machine) stop working

....

5 invent an excuse, story, etc.

....

6 look after a child until it is an adult

....

7 forgive and become friends again after an argument

....

8 fill space or time

....

2 Check your answers. Then choose the correct phrasal verb to complete the sentences.

1 They have decided that their marriage *has brought up / has broken down* and they're going to get a divorce.
2 When Jerry retired, he *made up / took up* golf.
3 After her parents died she *was brought up / was taken up* by an aunt.
4 We often argue but we always *make up / take up* soon after.
5 My job *makes up / takes up* all of my free time these days.
6 Sometimes it's better to *bring up / make up* an excuse than to tell the truth.
7 When they told her the bad news, she *brought up / broke down*.
8 I'm sorry to keep *bringing / taking* this *up* but you still haven't paid me the money you owe me.

3 Answer the questions.

1 Which hobby or sport would you like to *take up*?
2 When did you last *make up* an excuse? What was it?

Grammar

1 Present perfect review

1 Read the dialogue and choose the correct form, Past simple or Present perfect.

'*Did you hear / Have you heard* ¹ the news? Amy's getting married!'
'Who to?'
'Someone called Richard.'
'Really! How long *did she know / has she known* ² him?'
'Only about six months. Apparently, they *met / have met* ³ at a party. She says it *was / has been* ⁴ love at first sight.'
'*Did you meet / Have you met* ⁵ him?'
'Not yet. Lucy *told / has told* ⁶ me a lot about him, though.'
'When *did you see / have you seen* ⁷ Lucy?'
'I *saw / have seen* ⁸ her last week. We *went out / have been out* ⁹ for lunch. She *said / has said* ¹⁰ he's very good-looking!'
'Lucky Amy!'

2 Put the verb in brackets in the correct form, Past simple or Present perfect.

'Lucy ....¹ (phone) me last night. And guess what!'
'What?'
'Amy and Richard ....² (split up).'
'Really?'
'Yes. They ....³ (have) a big argument. It seems that Amy wants a church wedding but Richard doesn't.'
'What ....⁴ (happen) then?'
'Apparently, Amy's parents and Richard's parents ....⁵ (start) arguing, too. Amy's mother ....⁶ (say) that Richard wasn't good enough for her daughter, etcetera, etcetera ...'
'The usual thing then.'
'Yes. .... you ....⁷ (buy) them a present yet?'
'Not yet.'
'That's lucky! I .... already ....⁸ (send) mine. Do you think I'll get it back? I could do with a coffee percolator myself.'

2 Present perfect continuous (1)

Present perfect simple and continuous

Choose the most appropriate form, Present perfect simple or continuous. Both forms are possible in three of the sentences.

1 A: Why are you out of breath?
   B: I *'ve run/'ve been running*. I *'ve run/'ve been running* two kilometres.
2 Poor Janet. She *'s broken/'s been breaking* her arm.
3 Jason *has visited/has been visiting* Nepal many times.
4 I *'ve had/'ve been having* this headache since this morning.
5 I *'ve made/'ve been making* a cake. You can have a slice if you like.
6 A: Why is the kitchen in such a mess?
   B: I *'ve made/'ve been making* a cake.
7 How long *have you smoked/have you been smoking*?
8 Alex *has always been/has always been being* kind to me.
9 I *'ve studied/'ve been studying* English most of my life.
10 I *haven't spoken/haven't been speaking* to John for a long time. How is he?
11 I *'ve stayed/'ve been staying* with friends since I arrived.
12 *Have you finished/Have you been finishing* doing your homework yet?
13 A: How can you afford to buy a new car?
   B: I *'ve saved/'ve been saving*.
14 I *'ve meant/'ve been meaning* to invite Peter round for a coffee.
15 She *'s had/'s been having* a lot of problems with the car but not recently.

3 Present perfect continuous (2)

Rephrase these sentences by putting the verbs in brackets into the Present perfect continuous and making any other necessary changes.

1 I'm sorry now that I didn't tell you sooner. (wish)
   I've been wishing I'd told you sooner.
2 I don't know what to do with these old clothes. (wonder)
   ....
3 I'm sorry I didn't tell you the real reason. (wish)
   ....
4 I want to know where you got that dress. (want to ask)
   ....
5 I should have told you. (mean)
   ....
6 I should have written. (intend)
   ....
7 I'm really pleased to see you again. (look forward to)
   ....

8 I'm sorry now that I didn't tell you the truth. (wish)
   ....
9 Why did Mary and Richard split up? (want to know)
   ....
10 I don't know how to convince her I'm sorry. (wonder)
   ....
11 I really should have cleared out that cupboard. (mean)
   ....
12 What do you want for your birthday? (mean to ask)
   ....

Past simple and Present perfect tenses

Read the letter and choose the correct alternative.

Dear Jane

How are you? What *have you done/have you been doing* [1] since I last saw you? I'm sorry I *didn't write/haven't written* [2] before now but I *was/have been* [3] very busy recently.

I *'ve looked/'ve been looking* [4] for a new job. So far I *'ve sent/'ve been sending* [5] twenty job applications and I *had/have had* [6] four replies, which isn't bad! I *went/'ve been* [7] for two interviews already. A few days ago I *had/have had* [8] an interview for a job in Los Angeles! I *didn't hear/haven't heard* [9] from them yet though.

What else? Oh, yes. I *'ve learnt/'ve been learning* [10] to drive. Dad is giving me lessons. Amazingly, I *haven't crashed/haven't been crashing* [11] the car ... yet! I *have meant/have been meaning* [12] to ask you where you got your car. *Did you buy/Have you bought* [13] it from a garage?

Well, I'd better close now. I *'ve written/'ve been writing* [14] letters all evening and I'm getting writer's cramp.

By the way, Julie sends her love. Write back soon!

   Love,
   Denise

PS I *was invited/'ve been invited* [15] to Steve's birthday party. Are you going?

Writing

Expressing an opinion: adverbs

1 Read the article. Which of these statements is the best summary of what it is about?

1 The law regarding the legal age at which you can do things is unfair.
2 It is a waste of time having different legal ages for particular activities.
3 It is difficult to decide on a legal age for doing certain activities.

AGE and the LAW

There seems to be nothing harder than deciding at what age somebody should be allowed to do something – drive a car, drink alcohol, smoke cigarettes, play the Lottery.

Apparently, the British government is proposing to raise the age when you are allowed to buy cigarettes from 16 to 18. Should they therefore also consider raising the age at which people can gamble? At present this is 16 for the National Lottery and 18 for other kinds of gambling like betting on horse races. *Of course*, gambling is different from smoking, but that fact is of no help in reaching a decision about which of them a person should be allowed to do when.

There appears to be no logic to the law. Why should a person be allowed to play the Lottery two years before they are allowed to vote (at 18), and three more years before they are allowed to become a Member of Parliament (at 21)? Some people might argue that there is no point trying to stop anyone doing anything at any age. *Certainly*, some things are illegal no matter how old you are, yet people still do them.

The whole situation is very confusing and the questions are impossible to answer. I have one more of my own to add. Why is it that in Britain women can retire five years before men when women, as everyone knows, live longer than men? *Needless to say*, no one seems able to explain that anomaly. *Thankfully*, it is about to change.

2 Many adverbs and adverbial phrases give the reader information about the writer's attitude to what he or she is writing.

1 Write the adverbs and adverbial phrases below in the correct place in the table, according to their function.

As far as I'm concerned	Curiously	In my opinion	In my view	Sadly	Strangely

This is my personal opinion
   Personally, I think

I am sure of the facts / I agree with the facts
   Clearly

I am less sure of the facts
   As far as I know   *evidently*

I am surprised   *Surprisingly*

I am not surprised   *Not surprisingly*

I am pleased   *Fortunately*

I am not pleased   *Unfortunately*

2 Add the examples in italics in the article to the table. Check your answers.

3 Rewrite the sentences, using an appropriate adverb or adverbial phrase from the table. Write the adverb or adverbial phrase at the beginning of your sentence and put a comma after it.

a I wasn't surprised when John lost.
   Not surprisingly, John lost.

b I'm really glad it didn't rain as I had forgotten to take my umbrella.

c It is strange that Rachel doesn't resemble her twin at all.

d People should be allowed to vote when they are 16. That's what I think, anyway.

e I am not surprised that Sue didn't invite Mark.

f I've heard that you can get married in Scotland when you're 16.

g John was late, which was nothing unusual.

h I don't think that smoking should be allowed on any flight.

3 You are going to write one or two paragraphs describing the legal age at which people can drive, smoke, vote, etc. in your country.

1 First, note down some facts and how you and other people feel about the situation.

2 Expand your notes into paragraphs. Use a variety of adverbs and adverbial phrases to show how *you* feel about what you are writing.

3 Read through what you have written, correcting any mistakes in grammar, punctuation, and spelling. Are your ideas connected in an appropriate way? Have you included some 'attitude' adverbs?

4 When you are satisfied with what you have written, write out your final version.

Reading

Before you read

Decide whether you think the following statements are True or False.

1 ☐ Most animals can adapt to cold weather, but human beings can't.

2 ☐ If our body temperature drops three and a half degrees below normal, we begin to die.

3 ☐ Even when a person's body temperature drops below normal, they will still be able to think clearly.

4 ☐ If you are lost in the mountains in winter, the best thing to do is dig a hole in the snow and stay there.

5 ☐ Eskimos need to build fires inside their igloos to keep warm.

As you read

Check your answers. Correct any wrong statements.

Glossary

paradox (line 1): sth which is difficult to understand because it contains two opposite facts or characteristics

hibernate (line 12): (of some animals, e.g. bears) spend the winter in a sleep-like state

hallucination (line 31): belief that you see or hear sth which is not there

cagoule (line 40): light, waterproof jacket with a hood

whiteout (line 49): weather condition in which snow and clouds change the way light is reflected so that only very dark objects can be seen

The Winter's Tale

1   Winter is a season of paradox. It is the most magical season we know – a season of beauty, where snow transforms landscapes making even the most ordinary suburb, for a moment, quite beautiful.

2   Yet winter weather can also be very severe, and can be dangerous because of this. Human beings are totally unsuited to life in the cold. We evolved for life in Africa and unlike most animals and plants we cannot adapt to winter at all. We don't grow extra body hair then. We can't hibernate and if our body temperature drops just three and a half degrees below normal, we begin to die.

3   Every winter, mountain rescue teams across the world are called out to find people who have got lost in the snow. The climbers may have set out in fine weather but the weather in the mountains is unpredictable and can change from one moment to the next. Sergeant Graham Gibb of the mountain rescue team in Braemar, in the Scottish Cairngorm mountains, recalls how people lost in the snow act in extraordinary ways when their body temperature falls below normal. 'People start to have hallucinations and behave in totally irrational ways. Maybe they've got a big rucksack on their back. They think, "This is far too heavy. If I can just get rid of it, I'll be able to walk better." So they dump the rucksack. We come along looking for the person who's lost. First we find a rucksack, then we find a cagoule, and a bit further on we find a pair of boots. Eventually we come across the body.'

4   However, Braemar has also been the scene of many extraordinary stories of winter survival. In 1994, Jackie Greaves slipped on ice and fell down a mountainside. Amazingly unhurt, she wandered alone in a whiteout for two days before she was found by rescuers. In 1995 cross-country skier Andy Wilson broke records for survival after he spent three nights on the Cairngorms in a February blizzard. A helicopter spotted him stumbling through the snow on the morning of the fourth day.

5   What enabled both Jackie and Andy to survive was a knowledge of the life-saving properties of snow. Out in the wind on the mountain top the night

temperature had dropped to minus
39 degrees. In such temperatures
65 the human body will only last
about half an hour before it loses
consciousness. But inside a snow-
hole, protected from the wind and
insulated by the air in the snow, the
70 temperature is much higher – it
can be only slightly below freezing.

6 Snow is the most remarkable
material. As ecologist Peter
Marchand explains: 'In the West we
75 tend to regard snow as either
a nuisance or something to play
with. But we didn't always have the
technological advances that we
have today. In the past, snow was
80 one of the most useful materials
for surviving the winter. And even
today, you will find some people
who go to great lengths to keep
snow on their roof in winter
85 because they know about its
excellent insulating properties.'

7 Traditional cultures such as the
North American Indians and the
Inuit in northern Canada and
90 Greenland have always used snow
to make winter houses. Snow can
be cut into blocks to make an igloo
or hollowed out to make a quinzee,
the traditional home of the
95 Athabaskan Indians. With no
heating but the warmth of the
people inside it, a snow house can
be a nice snug place to spend the
night in winter.

8 Snow, then, has its dangers but
also its uses. We should keep this in
mind and use it to our advantage.
Savage Skies

Focus on vocabulary

1 Find words or phrases in the text with the meanings below. The paragraph number is given in brackets.

1 change completely (1) ....
2 bad; intense or difficult (2) ....
3 develop gradually from a simple form to a more complex one (2) ....
4 change to suit a new situation or use (2) ....
5 not using reason or clear thinking (3) ....
6 large bag used by walkers to carry things in (3) ....
7 get rid of sth you don't want (3) ....
8 severe snowstorm (4) ....
9 see or recognize sb when it is difficult to do so (4) ....
10 walk in a way which seems uncontrolled (4) ....
11 a thing, person, or behaviour which is annoying (6) ....
12 be prepared to do anything necessary to achieve sth (6) ....
13 prevent heat, sound, or electricity from passing through (6) ....
14 warm, comfortable, and sheltered (7) ....

2 Complete the sentences with a word or phrase you found in an appropriate form.

1 Toxic chemicals are often .... in the sea.
2 Human beings .... from apes.
3 A cat's fur .... it from the cold.
4 The car has been specially .... for disabled drivers.
5 The hurricane caused .... damage to the area.
6 .... conditions made the main roads impassable.
7 It can be very difficult to .... someone in a crowd.
8 I wish there was a direct train. It's a .... having to change trains.
9 Inside the .... he carried a small tent, some cooking equipment, and a change of clothes.
10 Jane lay in bed feeling .... and warm as the wind howled outside.
11 A few large mirrors can .... a small room, making it seem much larger.
12 The athlete .... to ensure that he was in peak physical condition for the race.
13 A phobia is an .... fear of something.
14 Not seeing the large stone, Philip .... over it and almost fell.

Understanding the text

1 How do human beings compensate for not being able to hibernate or grow extra hair?

....

2 What irrational arguments might a person lost in the snow make for getting rid of their cagoule and boots?

....

3 How exactly do you think Andy Wilson managed to survive?

....

4 In what ways could snow be regarded as a 'nuisance' to farmers, pedestrians, and motorists?

....

5 'In the past, snow was one of the most useful materials for surviving the winter.' What technological advances have replaced this use of snow?

....

Vocabulary

Topic vocabulary: weather

1 Put the words in the list into the correct group (1–4) ranking them from weakest to strongest.

blizzard   breeze   downpour   drizzle   fog   gale   hurricane

1 ⬭ (*wind*) ⬭ ⬭

2 (*mist*) ⬭

3 ⬭ (*shower*) ⬭

4 (*snow*) ⬭

2 Which adjectives go with the weather nouns? Choose from the list below. Some adjectives can be used more than once.

cold   dense   gale-force   gentle   light   strong   thick   torrential

1 *bright* .... *hazy* .... sunshine
2 .... fog
3 .... drizzle
4 .... snow
5 a .... breeze
6 a .... downpour
7 a .... wind

3 Check your answers. Then complete the sentences with an appropriate adjective and noun combination.

1 It was hot but the .... which came off the sea made the temperature bearable.
2 Walking through the .... was pleasant but exhausting and very cold.
3 We got caught in a .... and were absolutely soaked.
4 A .... blew from the north, bringing the temperature below freezing.
5 It was impossible to see where we were going in the ....
6 A .... fell, making the air feel damp.

Topic vocabulary: ways of walking

1 Use the example sentences below to help you match the verbs in italics with their meanings.

1 ☐ She *marched* into my office demanding an explanation for her dismissal.
2 ☐ We spent the afternoon *wandering* around the old part of the town.
3 ☐ I *stumbled* around in the dark trying to find the light switch.
4 ☐ After dinner in an expensive French restaurant, we *strolled* back to our hotel.

a walk in a way which seems uncontrolled
b walk quickly showing purpose and determination, especially of an army
c walk in a slow relaxed manner especially for pleasure
d walk slowly often without any clear purpose or direction

2 Complete the sentences with an appropriate verb in an appropriate form. Use each verb once.

1 The soldiers .... along the road and into the town.
2 I couldn't find your house. I've been .... up and down for ages.
3 They .... along the river bank enjoying the spring sunshine.
4 John .... down the stairs, still half asleep, to answer the door.

Phrasal verbs: *come* + particle

1 Match the phrasal verbs (1–6) with their meanings (a–g). Use a dictionary if necessary. *Come round* has two different meanings.

1 ☐ come across   a think of a plan or solution
2 ☐ come out   b happen unexpectedly
3 ☐ come round   c visit
  ☐ come round   d find accidentally
4 ☐ come up   e regain consciousness
5 ☐ come up against   f be revealed or made public
6 ☐ come up with   g be faced with a problem or difficulty

2 Check your answers. Then decide if the phrasal verbs in the following sentences are correct. Correct any wrong answers.

1 The first obstacle I *came up with* was making myself understood. No one spoke my language and I didn't speak theirs.

2 Jodie fainted when she heard the news but *came round* a few minutes later.

3 We had no idea what to do. Then Pete *came up with* a possible solution.

4 Andrea burst into tears and the whole story *came up*.

5 Why don't you *come round* to my place and we can talk about it over a coffee?

6 Look what I *came up against* while I was clearing out that cupboard.

7 There are no job vacancies at the moment. We will advertise any that *come round*.

3 Answer the questions.

1 Have you *come up* with any good ideas lately? What were they?

2 Have you ever *come across* something valuable?

Word-building: *-ness* noun endings

If you add *-ness* to some adjectives, it can mean *the state of being*. For example, *dark* + *-ness* means *the state of being dark*. For adjectives ending in *-y*, it is necessary to change the *y* to *i* first.

Complete the sentences with an appropriate noun formed from the adjectives below.

careless	friendly	happy	ill	kind	lonely	remote	weak

1 Because her .... was serious, she was kept in hospital under observation.

2 The Americans are well-known for their .... They will say 'hello' to total strangers.

3 We sent a letter thanking our hosts for their .... and hospitality.

4 It was your .... that caused the accident. You weren't paying enough attention.

5 Because of the .... of the island, hardly anyone goes there.

6 Many old people suffer from .... A dog makes a good companion.

7 The card read, 'We wish you every .... in your new job.'

8 Dieting is impossible for me; I have a terrible .... for chocolate.

Grammar

1 *can, could, be able to* review

1 Choose the correct alternative.

1 Be careful! Someone *can / could* steal your money.

2 *Am I able to / Can I* go now?

3 You *can't / couldn't* smoke here. This is a no-smoking area.

4 Ever since you gave me those tips, I *can / have been able to* stay on the horse without falling off.

5 It *can / is able to* be very cold in Canada in winter.

6 In the future we *can / will be able to* spend our holidays on the moon.

2 Complete the sentences with *can*, *could*, or the correct form of *be able to*. You will sometimes need to use the negative form. If two forms are possible, write them both.

1 '.................. I give you a lift?'
'I didn't know you .... drive! How long .... you .... drive?'

2 'Do you think you .... possibly lend me some money?'
'Sorry, I .... I haven't been paid yet.'

3 'Mr Smith? .... you let me leave at 3 o'clock today please?'
'You .... leave at 3 if you've finished those letters.'

4 Ever since I met David I .... understand why Denise likes him.

5 When I was 10 years old I .... speak fluent Italian but I .... remember a word of it now.

6 I'd love .... speak Greek as well as you do.

2 Ability and inability

1 Rewrite the sentences so that they have the same meaning as the original. Use the words in brackets and make any other necessary changes.

1 Patrick was able to change the wheel without any help. (manage) *Patrick managed to change the wheel without any help.*
(succeed) ....

2 I was able to swim when I was six but I wasn't able to swim underwater until I was eight.
(could) ....

3 Did you manage to persuade Jason to come?
(succeed) ....
(able to) ....

4 Have you succeeded in meeting your objectives?
(able to) ....
(manage) ....

2 Complete the story with the correct form of *could, be able to, manage,* or *succeed.* You may need to use the negative form.

Villagers flee flash floods

Witnesses say that they had never seen rain like it. 'You .... **¹ be standing one metre away from someone talking to them and not** .... **² see their face,' recalls one of the survivors.**

For the people who lived in the area, that night was a scene from hell. Barbara North was alerted by the family dog. 'I .... ³ hear the dog barking so I went to see what was the matter. The river was already up into our garden.' Without pausing to think, Barbara grabbed her young children and hurried them up to higher ground. 'It was so dark you .... ⁴ see your hand in front of your face. You .... ⁵ only see when there was a flash of lightning. Then everything was lit up for an instant and I .... ⁶ see cars and trees being swept along by the flood.'

Her neighbour Bob Barnes had hurried out of the house with his wife and two small daughters. He .... ⁷ climb onto the roof of their home and .... ⁸ help the others up just in time. 'It was awful,' recalls Bob. 'We .... ⁹ communicate with each other. All we .... ¹⁰ hear was this incredible noise.' The Barnes family was lucky. Parts of the house were washed away during the night but they survived.

Ambulance and rescue teams worked throughout the night and the next day and .... ¹¹ in rescuing all the residents. 'Fortunately the area isn't highly populated,' said a spokesperson. 'But if people hadn't reacted so quickly, it could have been a disaster.'

3 Articles

1 Complete the sentences with the appropriate article: *a, an,* or *the.* Where no article is required, write *X.*

1 I've never been involved in ..... very serious car accident. ..... worst accident I had was when I was driving my brother Jim home in ..... fog. ..... car left ..... road and hit ..... tree. We both had to go to ..... hospital but we were allowed to go ..... home ..... same day. Jim had ..... broken leg and I had ..... cuts and bruises.

2 I've always wanted to go to ..... United States. I'd like to travel to ..... east coast by ..... plane and then hire ..... car. I'd drive west stopping at all ..... towns I passed on ..... way. I'd spend ..... night in ..... cheap motel just like ..... ones you see in ..... movies.

3 Everyone in my family has been to ..... university. My brother and I both went to ..... University of Leeds. After finishing ..... university, I went to ..... college to train to be ..... teacher. I taught in ..... language school in ..... north of ..... Turkey for ..... year.

4 ..... children love ..... animals. ..... hamsters are ..... good pets for ..... young children. They are easy to look after. When I was young I had ..... cat. ..... cat's name was Smokey. It liked ..... fish and ..... milk. When it was ..... year old, it had ..... kittens, which surprised my father as he had thought it was ..... male cat.

5 There is ..... saying in English: '..... Englishman's home is his castle.' Certainly, ... English like to be private but there is ..... big difference between those who live in ..... south and those who live in ..... north. Not all ..... English people are ..... same.

2 Unjumble the words to make sentences. Begin with *The.*

1 the gets the it I hotter feel sleepier

....

2 better knows less the she the

....

3 sooner we the home the we sooner can finish go

....

4 worse you more the it is say the

....

5 more the I the have more earn pay tax I to

....

Writing

Cohesion

1 When we write, we make our writing easy to read in several ways. The text on the right could be improved in the ways shown.

2 You are going to read the preface to a book on the Outer Hebrides islands published by the Scottish Tourist Board.

  1 First, decide which of the following pieces of information about the islands you think it will contain.
  - Their location
  - Their population
  - Geographical features
  - Names of the main towns
  - Why you should visit the islands
  - Exact details of how to get there
  - The weather
  - Names of hotels and restaurants

  2 As you read, check your ideas. Make a brief note of any useful information given.

  3 Improve the text by rewriting the parts in bold. Use pronouns, reference words, etc.

3 You are going to write a short preface for a tourist book about a region in your country.

  1 Make notes in answer to the questions.
  - Where is the region located?
  - What are the special geographical features of the region?
  - What is the weather like at different times of the year? When is the best time to visit?

  2 Write out your notes into paragraphs, linking your ideas in an appropriate way.

  3 Read through what you have written, correcting any errors in grammar, punctuation, and spelling. Are your ideas appropriately linked? Does your text hold together?

  4 When you are satisfied with what you have written, write out your final version.

- Use reference words to refer back.
- Use synonyms when you can.
- Use conjunctions to show the relationship between the parts of the text.

He
Richard was late. ~~Richard~~ turned up five minutes before the
, *which*
film was due to start. ~~The fact that he was late~~ was nothing

new. I had been dating Richard for six months and I don't
we
think he had been on time more than once since ~~Richard and I~~
going out together
had started ~~dating~~.

'Sorry I'm late,' he apologized. 'The traffic was dreadful.'
This
~~The information that~~ the traffic was dreadful was an

excuse. The real reason he was late was simply that he
aren't on time
had left home late. I hate it when people ~~are late~~. I think it's
However *one*
extremely rude. Telling a lie, even a white ~~lie~~, is even worse.
So
Not being in any mood to accept his apology, I hurried
him
into the cinema without looking at ~~Richard~~. We took our

seats just as the lights went down.

- Use pronouns to refer to nouns.
- Use antonyms sometimes to give variety.
- Use 'one'. Don't repeat nouns.

❧ The Outer Hebrides ❧

THE OUTER HEBRIDES are a chain of islands about 210 km long which lie between 50–100 km off the north-west coast of Scotland. The total population of the 10 inhabited islands is just under 30,000, nearly all of whom live in small communities. There is only one town, [5] Stornoway, which is on the Isle of Lewis. **Stornoway** is the administrative capital and has about 8,000 inhabitants.

The islands are renowned for their superb scenery. **The superb scenery** includes silver shell beaches washed by turquoise and sapphire seas, a coastline with rocky cliffs, and wild, rugged [10] mountains. The whole area is a paradise for naturalists and walkers.

The best time to visit the Outer Hebrides is between May and August. **May, June, July, and August** are the sunniest and driest months. The average temperature then is 16–18°C. However, days without wind are rare. May and June are the months with most [15] sunlight. In fact, on a cloudless night it never gets totally dark.

A visit to the islands is not recommended during the rest of the year, however. Although the temperature rarely falls below freezing in winter, there are only four hours of daylight in the months of November and December. Add to this the fact that on a dull day it [20] may not get completely light. In addition, the winds can be gale-force from November onwards and usually bring with them heavy rain. **The winds** are quite pleasant in the summer months, however.

The Outer Hebrides are a unique corner of the British Isles, different in many ways from the other Scottish islands and the [25] mainland. **The Outer Hebrides** have a different culture, language, and scenery and are much more sparsely populated, yet each island has its own **different** character.

25 walks: The Western Isles

8

Reading

Before you read

1 What do you think would be the most stressful aspects of being on tour for members of a rock band? Name three.

....
....
....

2 What is a therapist? Why do you think members of a rock band might want to take a therapist on tour with them?

....
....
....

As you read

Check your ideas to **1** and **2** above. How many of your ideas are the same?

Glossary

on the road (headline): travelling, especially working as a sales representative or a performer

couch (headline): long, comfortable seat on which patients traditionally lie when they visit a psychiatrist

punishing schedule (line 30): tiring and busy programme of planned events

potent cocktail (line 36): dangerous combination of things

paranoid (line 38): abnormally suspicious of other people

macho (line 47): aggressively male

up-and-coming (line 66): likely to achieve success soon or in the near future

the be-all and end-all (line 84): the only thing that matters

On the road, on the couch

1 **Therapist Jacky Gerald helps touring rock stars cope with the pressures of**
5 **fame, as Peter Coleman saw.**

2 Gerald's job is to help rock musicians and other stars handle the pressures of fame and an
10 often ridiculous lifestyle. One key aspect of her work is to ease any tension among band members before a tour even starts.

3 'Obviously there are some bands
15 who always go on tour with the same people,' she says. 'But in the past 10 years or so, bands have been put together from people who may never have met before. We'll sit
20 down with them, look at the problems, and meet up with the band from time to time while they're on tour.'

4 Sometimes a band may even ask
25 Gerald to join the entire tour, in much the same way as they would take their own personal physician, chef, or trainer. When a group of people are on the road for months
30 at a time, with a punishing schedule, alternately bullied by the manager and worshipped by the fans, it does not make for the most stable atmosphere. Easy access to
35 drink and drugs can add to this potent cocktail.

5 Gerald says: 'In this business everybody is paranoid about everything. There are some
40 managers who are in therapy themselves, but nobody's supposed to know about it. And there are some managers who are worried that if they get their performing
45 artists some kind of support, it will affect their control over the band. It's a very macho business.'

6 Tackling this macho aspect of the music business is a part of Gerald's
50 longer-term work. Performers are often reluctant to admit they can no longer cope because they are afraid they will be thought weak.

7 She says: 'Providing they do what
55 they're supposed to do and say what they're supposed to say, that's fine. Anything beyond that and it's: "If you can't stand the heat, get out of the kitchen."'

8 Gerald set up her specialist practice *Rock 'n' Roll Therapy* with another therapist in the early 90s and has been working in this area ever since. She will not name any of
65 the clients she has worked with, but says they include both up-and-coming bands and some very well-known names.

9 'A lot of the boy bands come
70 from problem families and have a very low opinion of themselves. When someone in a fragile situation like this finds that the fans have turned against them, the effect can
75 be devastating,' Gerald says. 'If people learn to have a sense of self then it doesn't matter if, in the eyes of the world, they're great one day and rubbish the next – because they
80 know who they are. A lot of the work I do is about helping them to know themselves, and recognising that success or failure in the business isn't the be-all and end-all of life.'

The Guardian

9 The .... before the race started was almost unbearable.

10 They had always got on well in the past so she couldn't understand it when he .... her.

11 It was obvious from the weak excuse that he gave that he was .... to lend me his car.

12 It's not necessary to go to church to .... God, but most Christians do.

Understanding the text

1 What do you think the pressures of fame are?

....

2 Why do you think the writer uses the word *ridiculous* to describe a rock musician's lifestyle?

....

3 Why do you think the managers who are having therapy want to keep it secret?

....

4 What do you think the expression 'If you can't stand the heat, get out of the kitchen' means? Who might say this?

....

5 In what way could the effect be 'devastating' (paragraph 9)? Can you think of any rock stars who haven't been able to cope with the pressure of being famous? What happened to them?

....

Synonyms

Replace the words and phrases in italics with a word or phrase with a similar meaning from the list, using an appropriate form. There are two possibilities for two of the sentences.

afraid	as long as	begin	commence	concerned
establish	expect	field	now and again	whole	wonderful

1 What time does the actual ceremony *start*?
....

2 I go to the theatre *from time to time*. ....

3 The woman in front of me talked during the *entire* film.
....

4 We're *worried* that they'll be annoyed if they find out.
....

5 You can have Saturday off *providing* you work on Monday. ....

6 What am I *supposed* to do with this? ....

7 My father *set up* the business 20 years ago. ....

8 John has a degree in sociology and is an expert in this *area*. ....

9 It was a *great* party. Thanks for inviting us. ....

Focus on vocabulary

1 Find a word or phrase in the article with the meanings below. The paragraph number is given in brackets.

1 deal with a difficult situation [three words] (1, 2, 6)
....

2 essential or very important (2) ....

3 reduce (2) ....

4 feeling of nervousness before an important event (2)
....

5 frighten or hurt a weaker person (4) ....

6 love and adore (4) ....

7 result in; make possible (4) ....

8 help given in a difficult situation (5) ....

9 unwilling (6) ....

10 delicate; easily damaged or harmed (9) ....

11 start to dislike or disapprove of sb (9) ....

12 causing severe shock or distress (9) ....

2 Complete the sentences with the appropriate form of one of the words you found.

1 Be careful with that vase! It's very ....

2 I .... at school by some of the older pupils, who made me hand over my pocket money to them.

3 Bob Russell is a .... figure in local politics.

4 It's hard for single mothers .... with bringing up children on their own.

5 You can count on our .... if you ever need it.

6 Take two of these tablets. They will help to .... the pain.

7 The large print .... easier reading.

8 For many people the news of Princess Diana's death was
....

Vocabulary

Topic vocabulary: music and musicians

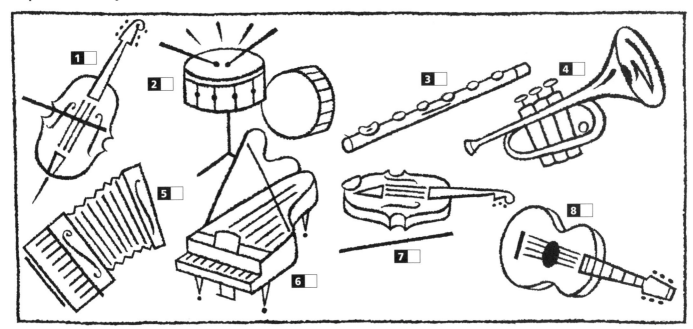

1 Match the musical instruments with the drawings.

a flute	b violin	c piano	d drums
e cello	f accordion	g guitar	h trumpet

Mark the stress on the words.

2 What is the name for the person who plays:

the drums? ....   the guitar? ....

the violin? ....   the piano? ....

Mark the stress on the words.

3 The following jumbled words are all connected with music. What are they?

1 Perform in several different towns, cities or countries.   ROTU ....

2 A recording which is made during a concert, not in a studio.   VILE ....

3 Music written in Europe between 1750 and 1830, for example, by Mozart.   SACCISALL ....

4 A record, tape, or CD containing several items by the same person.   BLAUM ....

5 A person who writes music.   POMCROSE ....

4 Answer the music questions on the next page.

Phrasal verbs: *make* + particle

1 What does *make* + particle mean in the sentences below? Match the phrasal verbs with their definitions.

1 ☐ Daniel walked into the room and *made* straight *for* the desk where the documents were kept.

2 ☐ There was so much noise that I couldn't *make out* what they were saying.

3 ☐ Can you *make out* the cheque to me please?

4 ☐ The band *is made up of* a drummer, two guitarists, and a vocalist.

5 ☐ I hate it when they aren't speaking to each other. I wish they'd *make up*.

6 ☐ I couldn't *make up* a good excuse for being late so I told the truth.

7 ☐ My boss said I could leave early every day next week to *make up for* having to work on Saturday.

8 ☐ It does not *make for* the most stable atmosphere.

a consist of; comprise

b invent (e.g. a story) sometimes in order to deceive

c manage to see, read, or hear sth

d compensate

e provide

f become friends again after an argument

g move, usually rather hurriedly, towards a particular place

h write out a bill, etc.

2 Complete the sentences with *make* in an appropriate form + an appropriate particle.

1 I can't .... what this says. Her handwriting is terrible.
2 Ritchie and Alice have decided to kiss and ....
3 A relaxed atmosphere and supportive colleagues .... a happy working environment.
4 The examination is .... of five papers.
5 The doctor .... a prescription for some sleeping pills.
6 'I'm starving!' Lucy said as she .... the fridge.
7 Can I take you out to dinner? I'd like to .... being so late the other day.
8 I told the children a story which I .... as I went along.

Grammar

1 Relative clauses review

1 Complete the sentences with an appropriate relative pronoun *who, which, that, when, why, where, what*. Add commas where necessary. There is sometimes more than one possibility.

1 Until I was eight we lived in a village called Stanway .... is now a suburb of Colchester.
2 The school .... I went to was a twenty-minute walk away.
3 Although it was near, it was up a big hill .... is why my sister and I always arrived out of breath.
4 I got on well with my sister Emily .... is two years younger then me.
5 We had a big garden .... we played when we weren't at school.
6 Our parents .... both worked hated having to spend so much time gardening.
7 That's the reason .... the garden of our second house was so small.
8 We used to visit our relations in London on Sunday .... my parents had the day off.
9 My father .... was an only child loathed visiting my mother's family.
10 Nevertheless, we always ended up doing .... my mother wanted.

• In which two sentences is no relative pronoun needed?

2 Rewrite this paragraph about Bob Marley including the extra information from the box. Add one piece of information to each sentence, put commas where needed, and make any other necessary changes.

, *whose full name was Robert Nesta Marley,*
BOB MARLEY ∧ **was a Jamaican** reggae singer. Marley wore his hair long in a distinctive style called 'dreadlocks'. This fashion was copied by young blacks and whites worldwide in the 1980s. The Rastafarians are a religious group which originated in Jamaica. Marley's songs popularized reggae music worldwide. Marley had one of his biggest hits with the song 'No Woman No Cry'.

Extra Information
- ~~Marley's full name was Robert Nesta Marley.~~
- He was a Rastafarian.
- The fashion was followed by most Rastafarians.
- Rastafarians worship the former Emperor of Ethiopia, Haile Selassie, as God.
- His songs often reflected his political beliefs.
- He was only 36 years old when he died of cancer.

2 Relative clauses

Complete the sentences in **1** and **2** by adding appropriate prepositions and relative pronouns from the lists. Add commas where necessary.

prepositions:	in	for	with	by	to

relative pronouns:	whom	which	who

1 Complete the sentences in a formal style.

1 The name *by which* Norma Jean Mortenson is better known is Marilyn Monroe.

2 Robert de Niro played the part of Vito Corleone in *The Godfather Part 2* .... he won an Oscar.

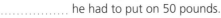

3 De Niro also won an Oscar for his performance as boxer Jake La Motta in the film *Raging Bull* .... he had to put on 50 pounds.

4 De Niro helped Sylvester Stallone put on weight for his role in the thriller *Copland* .... De Niro also stars.

5 The name .... Issur Danielovich Demsky is better known is Kirk Douglas.

6 Kirk Douglas .... his son Michael is constantly compared is best known for his role in the 60s film *Spartacus*.

2 Complete the sentences in an informal style.

1 The name *which* .... Norma Jean Mortenson is better known *by* .... is Marilyn Monroe.

2 The film *Pretty Woman* .... Richard Gere starred .... with Julia Roberts is one of his most successful films.

3 A popular sex-symbol of the 80s and 90s, Gere unexpectedly divorced supermodel Cindy Crawford .... he had been married .... for only three years in 1994.

4 *Dancing with Wolves* .... Kevin Costner won several Oscars .... is his most successful film to date.

5 *Waterworld* .... Costner invested a lot of his own money .... was one of the most expensive flops of the 90s.

6 The name .... American actor and director Allen Stewart Konigsberg is better known .... is Woody Allen.

3 Emphasizing words and structures

1 Make the information contained in the sentences more emphatic by adding an auxiliary verb (*do*, *does*, *did*) and making any other necessary changes.

1 I tried to warn him.
   I did try to warn him. ....

2 It may not seem like it sometimes but I love you.
   ....

3 He isn't very good at cooking but he tries.
   ....

4 You obviously don't remember but I told you about it.
   ....

5 I tried to explain but he wouldn't believe me.
   ....

6 I really think we should leave earlier.
   ....

7 Angela looks like her mother.
   ....

8 I told her you would be late.
   ....

2 Make the words in italics in the sentences more emphatic by adding one of the following words or phrases.

an emphatic pronoun, for example *myself*
very / really   indeed   on earth / ever

1 *I* know that being the eldest in the family has its disadvantages.
   I know myself that ....

2 My brother and I are *different*.
   ....

3 *Why* don't you want to go?
   ....

4 *The owners of the hotel* apologized to us.
   ....

5 *What* have you done to your hair? It looks awful!
   ....

6 *Kathleen Turner* collected the award.
   ....

7 It's *strange* you haven't met before.
   ....

8 We were *lucky* to get tickets.
   ....

Writing

Connecting ideas (2)

1 Read the article and decide which is the best title.

1 A Tribute to Charles Chaplin
2 The Chaplin Dynasty
3 Geraldine Chaplin: Her life and career

2 Read the article again.

1 Underline the words and phrases in the article which are used to give additional information, for example, *and*.
2 Check your answers before you continue.

3 Rewrite the information in the sentences to make one sentence. Use the words and phrases in brackets.

1 My grandparents on my father's side died before I was born.
My grandmother on my mother's side died before I was born.

(*both ... and*) *Both my grandparents on my father's side and my grandmother on my mother's side died before I was born.*

2 My father's father was called John. He was an excellent golfer. He was a talented artist.
(*who; and; too*) ....
....

3 My father was good at painting. His name was Robert.
(*whose; also*) ....
....

4 He painted landscapes. He painted portraits.
(*not only ... but also*) ....
....

5 My mother was quite good at art although she rarely had time for it.
(*as well*) ....
....

6 My mother's brother was called James. The husbands of two of my mother's sisters were called James. This was rather confusing.
(*as well; which*) ....
....

4 You are going to write a brief biography of your family in one or two paragraphs.

1 Think of some interesting facts. For example, did several family members have the same career or talent? Make some notes.
2 Expand your notes into one or two paragraphs. Use a variety of connecting words to join your ideas.
3 Read through what you have written, correcting any mistakes in grammar, punctuation, and spelling. Are your ideas connected in an appropriate way? Have you used a variety of connecting words and phrases where possible?
4 When you are satisfied with what you have written, write out your final version.

CHARLES CHAPLIN was born in 1889 and died in 1977 at the age of 88. As well as getting married three times, he had eleven children.

Charlie Chaplin (the clown)

Chaplin was well-known worldwide both as a comic actor and as a film director. In addition to the many short films he made, he also produced, acted in, and directed eleven full-length films, the last of which was *A Countess from Hong Kong* in 1967.

Most of Chaplin's children and grand-children have gone into some form of showbusiness too. Geraldine, Chaplin's eldest daughter, Christopher, his youngest

Geraldine Chaplin   Carmen Chaplin

son, and granddaughters Dolores and Carmen have all made acting their career, while daughters Victoria, Annette, and Josephine have worked in the theatre.

To date, Geraldine has had the most success. She has worked not only in Hollywood, where her most notable role was in the film *Doctor Zhivago*, but also in Europe. In the 70s she starred in many memorable films directed by the Spanish director Carlos Saura, who was her husband at the time. She has appeared in many films directed by the French film director Alain Resnais, as well. More recently she played the part of her own grandmother in Richard Attenborough's film about the life of her father, *Chaplin*.

9

Reading

Before you read

You are going to read a newspaper article about a 50-year-old married couple – Nadia and David Rice – who are going to take part in a 3,000 mile rowing race across the Atlantic. Before you read the article, predict the answers to the questions. Choose one answer only.

1 How do you think their friends reacted when they told them what they planned to do?
   a They thought they were crazy.
   b They were envious.
   c Both a and b.

2 How do you think their children, who are both students, reacted?
   a They were surprised.
   b They were excited.
   c They were worried.

3 How long do you think the race will last?
   a 45 days   b 90 days   c 200 days

4 What provisions do you think they will take with them?
   a Dried food.
   b Dried food and fresh water.
   c Tinned food and fresh water.

5 Why do you think they wanted to do it?
   a To show that they were not old yet.
   b Because of a need to explore.
   c Because they like rowing.

As you read

Check your answers. Are they the same or different?

Glossary

take the risk (line 8): do sth that exposes you to danger
kit (line 22): all the parts needed to make sth
adventure training centre (line 45): sports centre which specializes in outdoor sports, e.g. climbing, canoeing
capsize (line 69): cause a boat to turn over
tracking system (line 74): system which helps to locate sb or sth
emergency beacon (line 75): light that acts as a signal in an emergency
pump (line 121): machine that forces water, air, gas, etc. through sth

Rowing across the Atlantic

On Sunday David and Nadia Rice will set off from the Canary Islands on what will be the greatest challenge of
5 **their lives, the first rowing race across the Atlantic. Mike Rowbottom hears why they want to take the risk.**

This Sunday Nadia Rice and
10 her husband David, both aged 50, will set off from Tenerife for Barbados, some 3,000 miles* away, in a 24-foot† boat. They, along with 29 other pairs, will
15 be taking part in the first ever official Atlantic Rowing Race.

The entrants, who include two Olympic rowers, have each paid around $68,000 to take
20 part. They will compete in identical boats constructed from kits.

The Rices got a boat-building friend to construct their boat
25 for $17,000, and it has been the cost, more than anything else, which has come closest to putting them off their project.

'It is a lot of money. We have
30 managed to find sponsors to cover half our costs: things like travel and accommodation,' David says. 'But we will still be spending $34,000 of our own
35 money.'

When the Rices said good-bye to friends and family recently at their cottage in Somerton, Somerset, reactions
40 varied from 'Wish we could do it' to 'You're mad'.

David is familiar with the type of challenge the race will present – a former navy officer,
45 he runs an adventure training centre in Wales and has completed a single-handed Transatlantic crossing.

But for Nadia, who is a
50 teacher, it will be a new experience. 'I did consider pulling out a couple of times but David always managed to

persuade me not to,' Nadia
55 admits. The couple's children, Gareth and Sam – both students – are particularly surprised that their mother is prepared to risk her life on such a project.

60 David says, 'I don't think it's particularly risky. Anyway, life holds risks whatever you do. You could be run down by a bus tomorrow.' However, he
65 does concede that there are three main dangers: falling over the side in rough weather, being hit by a ship, and being capsized in a severe storm.

70 On the plus side is the fact that the hurricane season has finished, air temperatures are warm and all boats will be carrying satellite tracking sys-
75 tems and emergency beacons. Two ocean racing boats will also accompany them.

The Rices have been practis-ing rowing for 18 months now.
80 'On the day before we set off I am sure we will both be think-ing a lot about our children,' David says. 'But this race is going to be so demanding that
85 once it starts, we won't be able to concentrate on anything else.

'We will be rowing, navigat-ing, eating, sleeping, and rowing again. We won't have much time
90 to think about anything unless the weather is really awful and we have to stay in the cabin until the storm passes.'

The cabin is just 6ft 2in**

* 4,828 kilometres   † 7.31 metres

95 long so there will hardly be room to move, and if there are any arguments on their 90-day trip, it will make things even more unpleasant.

100 'We have been married for 26 years and I think we have become a good team. I think she would say I'm pretty quick-tempered, while
105 I would say she's fairly tolerant,' David admits.

The Rices have come up with a simple but revolutionary idea to make sure
110 their trip goes smoothly – a 'niceness contract'. 'We'll both have to sign it before we leave,' David says.

As for provisions, when
115 they leave next Sunday, they will be taking with them enough dried food to last the trip. This will be mixed with fresh water converted from
120 sea-water by means of a hand-operated pump, at the rate of one gallon†† per hour. 'We estimate that our water requirement will be four
125 gallons a day,' Nadia says.

The question David has been asked most in recent weeks is: Why are you doing it? 'I think,' he says, 'that the
130 answer lies in the common human need to explore. Once the start line is crossed, we are entering unknown territory.'

The Independent

** 1.88 metres   †† 4.54 litres

Focus on vocabulary

1 Match these words and phrases from the text (1–12) with their meanings (a–l).

1 ☐ challenge (line 4)
2 ☐ take part in (line 15)
3 ☐ project (line 28)
4 ☐ sponsor (line 30)
5 ☐ single-handed (line 47)
6 ☐ concede (line 65)
7 ☐ demanding (line 84)
8 ☐ room (line 96)
9 ☐ quick-tempered (line 104)
10 ☐ tolerant (line 105)
11 ☐ revolutionary (line 108)
12 ☐ rate (line 122)

a person or company that pays expenses connected with an event
b needing a lot of effort
c likely to become angry very quickly
d completely new and radical
e amount of space that sb or sth needs
f difficult task that tests someone's ability
g allowing sb to behave as they like even if you disapprove
h without any help
i activity with a particular aim
j participate
k measurement of how fast or how many times sth happens
l admit, often unwillingly, that sth is true

2 Check your answers. Then complete the sentences with one of the words or phrases in an appropriate form.

1 Teaching and nursing are stressful and .... jobs.
2 The government must do something about the rising .... of unemployment.
3 She isn't .... of other people's beliefs. In fact, she's prejudiced.
4 Mount Everest provides a .... for even the most experienced climbers.
5 John hasn't got a lot of money so he will have to give up athletics if he can't find a .... soon.
6 The hospital is trying out a .... new treatment on cancer patients.
7 'I didn't enjoy the party but I suppose it was nice of Barbara to invite us,' Philip ....
8 More than 20 people were involved in the .... to redesign the computer system.
9 He's very .... He shouts at the slightest thing.
10 Nick constructed the model .... It was all his own work.
11 My bedroom is quite small. There's only .... for a bed and a wardrobe.
12 Do you know how many countries .... the last World Cup?

Understanding the text

1 Why do you think the Rices had to pay such a lot of money to take part in the race?
....

2 Do you think the Olympic rowers would have any advantages over the other entrants? If you do, what do you think they would be?
....

3 Do you think the rowing trip will be easier for David or for Nadia? Why?
....

4 Why do you think they will be thinking a lot about their children the day before they go?
....

5 What do you think will be written on the 'niceness contract'? How important is it that they are nice to each other on the trip? Why?
....

Vocabulary

Topic vocabulary: travel

1 Complete the lists with the types of transport.

bicycle   bus / coach   car / taxi   helicopter
horse   plane   rowing boat   ship   train

board

disembark (from)

get in(to), get out (of)

get on, get off *bicycle*

2 Check your answers. Then complete the sentences with an appropriate verb from the lists in an appropriate form. Use each one once only.

1 When the bus finally arrived, I wasn't able to
.... because it was full.
2 The quickest way to get to Harrods is by Underground. Take the Piccadilly line and .... at Knightsbridge.
3 Passengers can .... from the front or rear doors of the aircraft.
4 .... the taxi, Zoe told the driver where she wanted to go.
5 Kate .... her car, locked the doors, and walked into the shop.
6 Will any remaining passengers for BA flight 348 to Nice please .... the plane now.

3 Complete the sentences with one of the words below in an appropriate form.

crossing   excursion   flight
journey   travel   trip   voyage

1 The Titanic sank on its first ....
2 Commuters are people who regularly .... a distance between home and work.
3 Travelling to Aberdeen from London involves an eight-hour train ....
4 My mother has gone on a coach .... to Belgium.
5 The price includes flights, half-board in a three-star hotel, and two full-day .... to places of interest.
6 The .... was delayed because ice had formed on the wings of the plane.
7 The ferry .... from Fishguard (on the west coast of Wales) to Rosslare (on the east coast of Ireland) is very pleasant when the sea is calm.

Collocations

1 Match one of the verbs *take*, *make*, *run* with an appropriate noun or phrase from the list below. Some of the nouns can collocate with more than one verb.

a bath   a break   a dislike   a car   a look   a risk
a speech   a suggestion   an interest   in the family

take

make

run

2 Check your answers. Then complete the sentences with an appropriate combination. Use an appropriate form of the verb and make any other necessary changes.

1 'Can I ....? Why don't we buy Julie a CD for her birthday?'
2 If more parents .... in their children's progress, they would do better at school.
3 Traditionally the father of the bride .... at the wedding.
4 I always take the bus. I can't afford .... yet; perhaps next year.

5 I think we're all tired. Let's .... and start again at 12.30.

6 .... at this, will you? Do you think the handwriting is the same?

7 I think I'll .... then have a nice long soak. It'll help me relax.

8 If you invest your money in stocks and shares, you ....; it's possible to lose it all.

9 Everyone in my family has had twins. It ....

10 I .... to Helen's boyfriend the moment I met him; he's very arrogant.

Phrasal verbs: *put off, pull out*

1 Read the different meanings of the phrasal verbs *put off* and *pull out*, then identify the meanings used in sentences 1–7.

Put off   a delay or postpone
            b extinguish (a light, TV, etc.)
            c make sb lose their concentration
            d make sb lose interest in sth

Pull out e decide not to continue an activity
            f leave
            g remove

1 ☐ Can you *put off* the lights when you go to bed?

2 ☐ The army will *pull out* of the city as soon as the situation stabilizes.

3 ☐ The dentist told me he would have to *pull out* the tooth.

4 ☐ Let's *put off* the meeting until everyone can attend.

5 ☐ Can't you be quiet? I'm trying to do my homework and you're *putting* me *off*.

6 ☐ Hendry had to *pull out* of the championship when he hurt his arm.

7 ☐ I had thought of becoming a nurse but the idea of having to work at nights *put* me *off*.

2 Complete the sentences with an appropriate phrasal verb making any other necessary changes.

1 Several people helped .... the girl .... of the river.

2 Don't .... till tomorrow what you can do today.

3 The train slowly .... of the station.

4 Three members of the team .... of the competition.

5 Don't forget .... the heater before you go to bed.

6 I was thinking of camping when I went to Ireland but Patrick .... me .... the idea.

7 People arguing in the back of the car really .... me .... my driving.

Grammar

1 Time and reason clauses review

1 Complete the sentences with a suitable word or phrase from the list. Use each word once only.

after   as   as soon as   because   before
since   until   when   while

1 David and Nadia Rice want to row across the Atlantic .... it's a challenge.

2 .... the kits arrived, their friend started building the boat.

3 .... they leave, they won't have time to think about the children.

4 They will have to pay $34,000 of their own money .... they didn't find enough sponsors.

5 .... the cabin is so small, they will need to get on.

6 .... one of them is operating the pump, the other will probably be rowing.

7 .... they can eat the food, they will need to add fresh water.

8 Their children will probably worry .... they are on dry land again.

9 .... they arrive in Barbados they will be able to enjoy a well-earned rest.

2 Put the verbs in brackets in the sentences into the correct tense.

1 The first time I went on an adventure holiday, I didn't do any exercise before I .... (go).

2 I hadn't realized that before you .... (go) on that type of holiday you need to be fit.

3 So, take my advice. As soon as you .... (book) your holiday, if not before, get down to the gym.

4 However, if you haven't done any exercise for a while, it is a good idea to have a check-up before you .... (start) exercising.

5 Don't overdo things because it .... (have) a negative effect on your body.

6 Build up gradually until you .... (be able to) do the exercises quite easily.

7 Finally, don't forget to drink plenty of water while you .... (exercise).

8 Hopefully, you won't have the same problems that I did when I .... (come back) from my holiday!

2 Participle clauses

1 Rephrase the participle clauses in the sentences with a relative clause (*who*, *which*); a time clause (*when*, *while*); a reason clause (*because*, *as*) or two main clauses joined by *and*. Use each word at least once.

1 Adventure training centres are designed for people wanting to do outdoor activities.

....

2 Arriving at the adventure training centre, I was surprised to see that there were people of all ages there.

....

3 Not having been to an adventure training centre before, I didn't know what to expect.

....

4 Putting on my boots, I chatted to the person next to me.

....

5 Having been three times previously, he was an expert.

....

6 We left the changing rooms together and walked towards a group of people standing with the instructor.

....

7 As I wanted to try canoeing, I was told to follow the path going down to the river.

....

8 Not having been canoeing before, I was a bit nervous.

....

2 Rewrite the following sentences. Include a participle clause in each one.

1 While I was fastening my helmet under my chin, I suddenly remembered that I couldn't swim.

....

2 I made an excuse and ran back towards the main building.

....

3 I apologized to the instructor and asked if I could try another activity.

....

4 I wasn't very keen to try mountain climbing as I am afraid of heights.

....

5 I couldn't go windsurfing either because I couldn't swim.

....

6 Because I had already paid in advance, I felt I should do something.

....

7 In the end, I decided that outdoor sports were not for me and went home.

....

3 Cause and effect

Decide whether the following sentences are correct. Correct any wrong sentences using an appropriate structure from the list in an appropriate form.

bring about	cause	lead to	make	result in

1 Death, divorce, and moving house are the top three events which *cause* stress.

2 Not surprisingly, financial problems and unemployment *result in* you feel stressed too.

3 But what can you do when even holidays *make* people to become stressed?

4 When you are stressed out the smallest thing can *lead to* you explode.

5 A certain amount of stress is beneficial. It can *make* us perform better.

6 But too much stress over a long period can *lead to* serious health problems.

7 If left untreated, these could even *make* a heart attack or nervous breakdown.

8 On the plus side, regular exercise can *bring about* a reduction in stress levels.

Writing

Connecting ideas (3)

1 You are going to read a story with the title 'An eventful journey'. Before you read it, predict some of the transport problems the writer might have had as he travelled by train, tube, taxi, and plane from the north-east of England to Spain one summer.

He might have missed his train. ....

Perhaps the train was full and he had to ....

stand. ....

2 As you read the story, see how many of your ideas are the same.

3 a Read the story again and underline all the sequence words and phrases. The first two have been done for you. There are 17 in total.

   b Match the words and phrases below with words and phrases in the story with a similar meaning.

   at long last   ....

   the following (morning)   ....

   at once/immediately   ....

   up to that point/until then   ....

   just then   ....

4 Complete the sentences with an appropriate word or phrase from the list. Use a dictionary to check the meaning of any words you are not sure of.

| after a while | afterwards | meanwhile |
| next time | previously | |

   1 I decided to book my flight with Virgin Airlines. ...., I had always flown to Paris with Air France.

   2 The passengers boarded the plane. ...., the luggage was being stored in the hold.

   3 I waited next to the luggage belt. ...., I realized that my suitcase wasn't going to appear.

   4 My luggage had been left behind at Heathrow Airport. .... I will travel by train.

   5 At first I was very angry. .... I realized that these things happen.

An eventful journey

I was not particularly looking forward to returning to Spain. It would involve a bus journey, two train journeys, one underground journey, and a two-and-a-half hour flight. I hate travelling and am only happy when I reach my destination.

5 <u>After</u> saying goodbye to my family in Alnwick, I got on the Newcastle bus arriving at Newcastle bus station <u>just over an hour later</u>. I took a taxi to the railway station, where I caught my first train. After an uneventful journey lasting an hour and a half, we arrived in Carlisle just before 11 p.m. I had three hours to kill
10 before I could board the overnight train to London. I passed the time drinking endless cups of coffee.

Finally at 2 a.m. the train pulled in. I got on and found my seat. I had hoped to be able to sleep but the other passengers in my compartment had different ideas and spent the whole journey
15 talking and playing cards. By the time we reached London early the next morning, I was in a state of exhaustion. I didn't realize then that my problems hadn't even started.

I walked towards the underground. Straightaway, I realized that something was wrong. Nobody else seemed to be heading in
20 that direction. When I got nearer, I saw a sign. There was a strike. No problem. I would take a taxi to Victoria Station instead. I approached the taxi rank. Up to that moment I had simply been tired. Now I was starting to get worried. A long queue snaked into the distance. I joined it.
25 The minutes passed and I got more and more agitated. In the end I pushed my way to the front and begged the woman who was getting into the taxi to let me share. When I eventually got to Victoria, I discovered that the airport train had just left. There wouldn't be another one for an hour. I would miss the flight.
30 I rushed outside to the taxi rank. The fare was ridiculous but I had no choice. Over an hour later I stood breathless at the departure desk begging the clerk to let me board. The plane was due to leave in fifteen minutes. You can imagine how I felt when she told me the flight had been delayed. It wouldn't be leaving for
35 another six hours. At that moment I didn't care if I ever travelled anywhere again.

5 You are going to write a story describing a journey you have been on. It can be real or imaginary.

   1 Think of some ideas. For example: How did you travel? What went wrong? How did you feel? Make some notes.

   2 Expand your notes into paragraphs. Remember to begin a new paragraph for each new idea.

   3 Read through what you have written, correcting any mistakes in grammar, punctuation, and spelling. Is your journey described in an interesting way? Is your writing cohesive? Have you used a variety of time sequencing words and phrases?

   4 When you are satisfied with what you have written, write out your final version. You could give it to a friend to read and ask them what they think.

Reading

Before you read

How much do you know about lying?
Are these statements True or False?

1 ☐ Children learn to lie after the age of five.
2 ☐ Women are generally better liars than men.
3 ☐ One third of what we tell our partners is a lie.
4 ☐ We look someone in the eye when we are lying.
5 ☐ When we lie we gesticulate more with our hands.

As you read

1 Check your ideas. Correct any wrong statements.

2 These headings are missing from the article. Decide where each one goes.

1 It's the truth, darling!
2 Getting to the heart of the matter
3 Liars start young
4 Watch out for babyface
5 Look me in the eye and say that
6 Masters of deception
7 Smiling, happy liars

Glossary

The art of deception (headline): ability to make sb believe sth which is not true
swear blind (line 14): say sth is absolutely true
vice-versa (line 26): (Latin) opposite to what has been said
give the game away (line 29): reveal a secret, especially by accident
put on (line 31): pretend; not real
crow's feet (line 34): lines in the skin around the outer corner of the eye
wry (line 39): showing you find a difficult situation quite amusing
forced (line 40): produced with effort; not sincere
inbuilt (line 55): quality people have from the time they were born
pupils dilate (line 67): black central part of the eye gets bigger
give-away (line 71): look or remark that reveals a secret without intention

The art of deception

1 If he can read your thoughts, he'll cheat you before you can say: 'Liar!' Sanjida O'Connell reveals the mind-reading secrets of life's most skilled deceivers.

2 Did you know that we're all natural-born psychologists? It's true.
5 Psychologists have discovered that mind-reading (the ability to work out what people are thinking) is a universal human ability developed during childhood.

3 While being able to mind-read is essential for successful social relationships, it is also the skill behind lying. Only by imagining what
10 goes on in someone's head is it possible to manipulate and deceive them. Let's look at some of the facts about lying.

a

4 It takes the first five years of our life to learn how to lie but we soon do. You probably remember swearing blind as a child that you hadn't
15 been anywhere near the biscuit tin – even though your face was covered with chocolate.

b

5 Women tend to be more skilful and imaginative liars than men. Several studies show that girls tend to do better in mind-reading tests
20 at a slightly younger age than boys.

c

6 You'd probably think that we are more honest with those closest to us. But, when it comes to our partners, studies indicate that approximately one
25 third of everything we tell them is, in fact, a total fabrication. And vice-versa.

d

7 As regards facial expressions, there are a number of muscles that give the game away.
30 A genuine smile can be distinguished from a 'put on' one thanks to the *orbicularis oculi*, a muscle near the eye which causes crow's feet to appear in
35 the skin. This muscle will only contract when people are genuinely happy.

8 The human face is able to perform no fewer than 19 other smiles. For example a 'wry' smile is the sign of a liar while
40 a 'forced' smile is usually less

symmetrical than a real one. Each kind of smile is controlled by a different part of the brain.

e _____

9   When we lie, our heart beats faster, we breathe more rapidly, and we perspire more. This can be measured by polygraphs (lie-detector tests). However, an innocent person being questioned
50 about a murder might be so nervous that they exhibit all these symptoms, whereas the real murderer could be capable of staying absolutely calm. About two per cent of the population seem to have an
55 inbuilt ability to know when someone is lying. In psychological tests they can pick out the ones who are cheating 100 per cent of the time.

f _____

10   When we lie, we try to control our facial expressions and look the person to whom we are lying directly in the eye. It doesn't work – our natural instinct is to avoid looking at them. Besides, our
65 body language gives us away. Liars gesticulate less with their hands, they blink more, their pupils dilate, their voices rise and they tend to fiddle with their clothes or their hair.

70 g _____

11   Despite all these give-aways, most of us can be taken in by good liars: people that psychologists refer to as 'natural performers'. This doesn't mean
75 that they have perfected the art of controlling their *orbicularis oculi*: it means they have the physical advantage of a round, baby-shaped face; they are handsome and charismatic, and they
80 appear to be trustworthy – making it easy for them to take the rest of us in.

Focus magazine

Focus on vocabulary

1 Find words or phrases in the text with the meanings below. The paragraph number is given in brackets.

1 make facts, etc. known (1) ....
2 find the answer to sth (2) ....
3 control or influence sb or sth (3) ....
4 become smaller (7) ....
5 really (7) ....
6 having two halves which are exactly the same (8) ....
7 select; choose (9) ....
8 make movements with your hands and arms while talking (10) ....
9 open and close your eyes quickly (10) ....
10 keep moving or touching sth (10) ....
11 having great personal charm which can attract, influence, and inspire people (11) ....
12 able to be trusted because they are reliable and responsible (11) ....

2 Complete the sentences with a word or phrase you found in an appropriate form.

1 To work in a bank you must be completely ....
2 Metals expand with heat and .... as they cool.
3 The sun shone directly in his eyes making him ....
4 When I'm nervous, I .... with my ears.
5 JF Kennedy, one of the most .... American presidents of the 20th century, charmed everyone who met him.
6 I think you should accept her apology. She really is .... sorry.
7 I can't .... who told me. I promised not to.
8 Can you help me with this mathematical equation? I can't .... the answer.
9 A skilful barrister can .... a jury into believing his client is innocent.
10 The paintings on that wall are not .... One is a bit higher than the other.
11 If you ask a child if they'd like a chocolate, they always .... the biggest one.
12 I find it very difficult to talk without ....; using my hands seems to help what I want to say.

Understanding the text

1 According to the information in the text and your own views, what makes someone a good liar?

....

2 When might you give a 'forced' smile? Think of some possible situations. What other kinds of smile can you think of?

....

3 Think of some examples of lies which wives might tell their husbands, husbands might tell their wives, and children might tell their parents, and their reasons for telling the lies.

....

Vocabulary

Topic vocabulary: crime

1 Match the crimes with their definitions. Use a dictionary to help you if necessary.

---
blackmail   forgery   fraud   manslaughter
murder (US homicide)

---

1 deliberate illegal killing of a human being ....

2 making a copy of sth in order to deceive people (e.g. banknote, passport, signature) ....

3 deceiving sb in order to make money or obtain goods illegally ....

4 demanding money from sb in return for not revealing secret information about them ....

5 killing a person illegally but not intentionally ....

2 Read the definitions, then complete the words by adding the missing letters.

1 to do a crime   C☐M☐☐T
2 a person who does a crime   C☐☐M☐☐A☐
3 the group of people in a court of law who decide if the accused is innocent or guilty   J☐☐Y
4 the decision reached by the above in a court of law   V☐☐D☐☐T
5 the punishment given by a court of law   S☐N☐E☐C☐
6 a small room in a prison where prisoners are kept   C☐L☐
7 declare officially that sb is guilty of a crime   C☐NV☐C☐

3 Complete the sentences with one of the words from exercises **1** and **2** in an appropriate form.

1 She bought the work of art thinking that it was genuine when in fact it was a ....

2 The .... was made up of 12 people from all walks of life.

3 The number of crimes .... by children under 16 is increasing.

4 The prisoners were allowed out for exercise but spent the rest of the time in their ....

5 Many .... find it difficult to get a job after they are released from prison.

6 It took the jury two days to reach a .... of not guilty.

7 David Dodd, who had not paid his taxes for ten years, was found guilty of ....

8 The woman is serving a life .... for the .... of her husband, whom she had poisoned over a six-month period.

9 The driver of the car, John Bridges, was .... of .... The judge decided his dangerous driving had led to his girlfriend's death.

10 'I'm not going to pay you to keep quiet. That's .... !'

Colour idioms

A *white lie* is a small lie often told to avoid hurting people's feelings. Complete the sentences by adding one of these colours. Check your ideas in a dictionary.

---
black   blue   green   red   white

---

1 Martin was always jealous of his younger brother because he was his mother's ....-*eyed boy*.

2 I'm hopeless with money. I'm always *in the* ....

3 After twenty years, my mother's brother turned up *out of the* ....

4 He's promised me a contract but I won't believe it till I see it *in* .... *and* ....

5 He went *as* .... *as a sheet* when I told him the police had called.

6 ....-*collar workers* do manual jobs or work in factories.

7 ....-*collar workers* work in offices or work in business or one of the professions.

8 I was .... *with envy* when I saw Jason's new car.

Phrasal verbs: *work out, take in*

1 The phrasal verbs *work out* and *take in* have several different meanings. Read the example sentences (1–7) and match the verbs with their meanings (a–g).

1 ☐ I couldn't *work out* why the house was in darkness. Then I remembered they were away.

2 ☐ Things *are working out* really well for Andrew in his new job.

3 ☐ Body-builders are obsessed with *working out*.

4 ☐ You can't fool me! I won't be *taken in* so easily again.

5 ☐ We *took* him *in* as he had nowhere to live.

6 ☐ There was too much information to *take in* all at once.

7 ☐ We *took in* a show when we were in New York.

a find a solution to a problem

b go to see a film, museum, etc. when you are visiting a place

c deceive

d allow sb to live in your house as a favour or as a paying guest

e understand or remember sth you have heard, seen, or read

f do physical exercise in order to be fit and strong

g happen and develop in a satisfactory way

2 Complete the sentences with the phrasal verb *take in* or *work out* in an appropriate form, making any other necessary changes.

1 He goes to the local gym twice a week to ....

2 It was kind of you to .... me .... when I had nowhere else to go.

3 I can't .... why Julia isn't speaking to me.

4 Jane .... by Gary's story and agreed to lend him some money.

5 The new system isn't .... very well.

6 We always .... a play or an exhibition when we're in London.

7 Sara was so shocked she couldn't .... what the doctor was saying.

Grammar

1 Passives review

1 Complete the sentences with one of the verbs below in the correct form of the passive. You will need to use the negative form once.

---

affect   boost   make   persuade   pay   sell

---

1 Almost half of the shoes which .... in the United States these days are trainers.

2 Nowadays major sporting superstars .... huge sums of money to advertise products.

3 Sales of sports goods in general .... by the interest in fitness and running in the 80s and 90s.

4 Many parents .... to buy expensive top brands by their fashion-conscious children.

5 Trainers and other goods .... in many countries.

6 Surprisingly, sales of trainers .... by the fact that they have been a fashion item for so many years.

2 Put the verbs in brackets into the correct form of the passive.

The production of counterfeit goods is rising. Top brand names ....¹ (reproduce) illegally all over the world and billions of dollars ....² (lose) each year in tax revenue. In fact, 5% of the world's trade ....³ (represent) by this black market. Frequently counterfeit goods ....⁴ (buy) by people who think that they are the real thing. Those that suspect they aren't, buy them because of the price. Fake perfume, for instance, can ....⁵ (buy) at a quarter of the price of the real thing. Top companies are complaining that their reputations ....⁶ (damage) by inferior products, and although new anti-counterfeiting laws ....⁷ (introduce) in Europe, the situation has not improved. This is partly because the production of counterfeit goods ....⁸ (organize) by some of the most sophisticated criminal organizations in the world.

3 Cross out the agent (*by ...*) in these sentences where it would be more usual to leave it out.

1 He has been sentenced to five years' imprisonment by a judge.

2 The information was passed on to me by William.

3 The actress wasn't recognized by anyone as she was wearing dark glasses.

4 He was warned by someone not to tell the police.

5 We have been invited to the dinner by the President.

6 Shoplifters will be prosecuted by the owner of the shop.

7 The man was charged with dangerous driving by the police.

2 Passive constructions

You are preparing a news report for a radio station. You are not sure whether all the information you have received is correct and you have underlined any unconfirmed information in your notes. Write up your news report using the present passive form of the verbs in brackets.

1 <u>Pop star Michael Jackson has got married again.</u> (report) <u>His new wife is French.</u> (believe)

   Pop star Michael Jackson is reported to have got married again. His new wife is believed to be French.

2 There has been another earthquake in Southern California. <u>Several buildings have been damaged.</u> (report) <u>The town of Malibu has been worst affected.</u> (believe) <u>There are no casualties.</u> (think)

   ....

   ....

3 Part of Roberto's nightclub in Leeds has been destroyed by fire. <u>The fire started in the basement.</u> (believe) <u>It was started deliberately.</u> (believe)

   ....

   ....

4 Reports are just coming in that thieves have broken into the National Art gallery. <u>Two paintings by Renoir and one by Picasso are missing.</u> (say) <u>One of the robbers was working in the museum as a security guard.</u> (believe)

   ....

   ....

3 The pronoun *it*

1 Make the part or parts of the sentence underlined more emphatic. Use the structure *It is/was ... who/that ...* in an appropriate form.

1 <u>Mary</u> isn't coming. <u>Marie</u> is coming.

   It's Marie who/that is coming, not Mary. It isn't Mary who/that is coming, it's Marie.

2 <u>My father</u> taught me to play the guitar, not <u>my brother</u>.

   ....

3 I didn't tell <u>Mary</u>. I told <u>Sharon</u>.

   ....

4 Damien is arriving <u>the week after next</u>, not <u>next week</u>.

   ....

5 <u>Pete</u> took the decision. <u>I</u> didn't.

   ....

6 I don't dislike <u>the taste</u> of garlic. I dislike <u>the smell</u> of garlic.

   ....

2 Rewrite the sentences with *It ...*

1 Eating spaghetti without a spoon is hard.

   It's hard to eat spaghetti without a spoon.

2 Talking is good.

   ....

3 Seeing him go made me sad.

   ....

4 Making the decision was difficult.

   ....

5 Giving up smoking hasn't been easy.

   ....

6 To get to Paris from here takes just over an hour.

   ....

3 Complete the sentences with *it* + *that* clause or *it* + infinitive. Make any other necessary changes.

1 Salaries will need to be frozen. The government has made this clear.

   The government has made *it clear that salaries will need to be frozen.*

2 Making new friends is difficult for me.

   I find *it difficult to make new friends.*

3 Not many people came to the party, which was a shame.

   We thought ....

4 Studying with the television on is impossible for me.

   I find ....

5 I've taken up skiing. Nick thinks this is funny.

   Nick thinks ....

6 She didn't phone me to tell me she would be late. This was unusual.

   I thought ....

7 Writing with a broken finger was hard.

   I found ....

Writing

Supporting statements

In Unit 3 we looked at *topic sentences* and why we use them in a piece of writing. In this unit we will look at the function of the sentences which follow the topic sentence. We can call these sentences *supporting statements*. We use them to support the topic sentence by giving additional information. There must be a strong link between the topic sentence and the supporting statement(s).

1 Before you read the article, look at the headline.
Do you think the writer will be in favour of or against the Internet?

....

2 Parts of the text have been removed from the article. As you read the article, choose which extract (1–4) fits each gap. Check your answers before going on to **3**.

3 There are links between each topic sentence and its supporting statement(s). What do the following reference words in the supporting statements refer to?

1 They (extract 1) ....

2 It (extract 2) ....

3 This (extract 3) ....

4 They (extract 4) ....

4 You are going to write a few paragraphs which support the opposite point of view to that given in the article. You can use the topic sentences and the ideas for supporting sentences in the box if you like.

1 Before you start writing, think of some ideas which support your topic sentences.

2 Expand your ideas into sentences. Make sure that there is a link between your supporting statement(s) and the topic sentence.

3 Write out your ideas into paragraphs, linking them in appropriate ways.

4 Read through what you have written. Are your views expressed clearly? Does your text hold together? Correct any errors in spelling, punctuation, and grammar that you find and give your text to someone else to check.

5 When you are satisfied with what you have written, write out your final version.

---

1 *The Internet is a rich source of information.*
What can you find on the Internet? Give a variety of examples.
How might it be particularly useful for school-age children?

2 *Using the Internet is extremely time-saving.*
How can it save you time?
(For example, shopping from home, researching information.)

3 *You communicate more with people, not less, if you are on-line.*
Compare e-mail with phone calls and letters.
What advantages are there?

4 Write your own summarizing final topic sentence and supporting sentences.
(For example, the most useful technological advance yet? Future uses?)

Virtually no life at all

The Internet was born to almost universal acclaim, but it has a dark side, too.

a

We are in danger of creating a generation of Internet introverts, who can only interact with others when they are sitting behind a computer screen.

b

Parents need to take positive action to stop the growth of this new social phenomenon.

c

The Internet is an artificial world.

d

Extracts

1 They do everything on-line: they write on-line, they order books and pizzas on-line, they view the world from on-line.

2 It is a world without touch, which ignores years of social evolution. We need to ensure that it is not the only world that our children grow up in. Otherwise, our children may end up preferring it to the real, more loving but more frightening world outside.

3 This concerns the effect on people who spend twelve hours on-line, isolated from other people, from social functions, from the breeze of a spring day, or the touch of someone's hand.

4 They should set limits on the amount of time they allow their children to play on computers. They should find time to spend with their children doing other real activities.

Reading

Before you read

You are going to read an article about a couple who are passionate about volcanoes. First, guess which two of the following words will not be used in the text.

screaming	awful	experience (n)
waterfall	coughed	ash
experts	unpredictable	

As you read

Check your ideas.

Glossary

erupting (line 8): throwing out burning rocks, lava, etc.

churn (line 11): (of liquids) move about violently

bubble (line 11): boil

shield (line 14): large piece of metal carried on the arm to protect the body when fighting

molten (line 20): (of rocks, metals) made liquid

make an offering (line 26): offer sth to a god as a gift

exchange vows (line 27): make promises during a marriage ceremony

lava flow (line 28): river of hot, liquid rock

vulcanologist (line 37): scientist who studies volcanoes

Volcano chasers

Steve and Donna O'Meara are passionate about volcanoes. They live in Hawaii, a group of islands created entirely by volcanic activity, in a village called Volcano.

a _____. He thought she was very attractive. And on their second date he was determined to impress her. 5

' b _____. Steve called me at my office and said, "How would you like to see an erupting volcano?" and I said, "Sure". 18 hours later we were flying in a helicopter over Kupaianaha, which is a Hawaiian lava lake about 213m wide. 10 It was churning and bubbling and I was screaming. And that was it. I was hooked. It's the most memorable experience I have ever had in my life.'

c _____. They are called 'shield' volcanoes because they look like overturned saucers. The eruptions are very gentle. 15

' d _____. It was a large fire mountain 1km long. When it started off it sounded like a waterfall. But then more gas started coming out than lava and it was breathing, it was choking, it was inhaling. And then it coughed and spat out these molten rocks high up into the air ... 30 ... 60 metres into the air. 20 And this happened over and over again until that was it ... it just died.'

e _____. When Steve and Donna decided to get married, they were both keen for the ceremony to take place on a volcano. They got permission from the Hawaii National Park 25 and flew out to Kilauea, where they made an offering of lilies to Pelé, the goddess of the volcano. Then they exchanged vows on a lava flow that was about three hours old.

' f _____. After we got married, we both gave up our jobs and now we spend all our time travelling all over the world 30 taking photographs of volcanoes.'

However, in spite of their love affair with volcanoes, the O'Mearas are very aware of the dangers.

' g _____. That's why when we visit volcanoes we always go up with the experts. They know the land best. Volcanoes 35 are always unpredictable. People die every year. Even vulcanologists and geologists who know these volcanoes very well die. '

' h _____. I'd rather have ten minutes of something wonderful than a lifetime of nothing special, wouldn't you?'

Savage Earth

Donna and Steve O'Meara

Comprehension

Read through the sentences (1–9) and choose the sentence which best fits each gap (a–h) in the article. There is one extra sentence you will not need to use.

1 Hawaiian volcanoes have a characteristic form and style of eruption.
2 There is always a dark side to volcanoes so you must always be on your guard and ready for anything.
3 This continues and so you get a chain of islands formed.
4 For two people with such a fascination for volcanoes, it is no surprise that they have settled in Hawaii.
5 It was the day before Christmas Eve.
6 We know our lives are short so we make the most of every moment.
7 I'll never forget my first eruption.
8 Steve fell for Donna the moment they were introduced.
9 I used to be an astronomy teacher and Donna used to work in an office.

Focus on vocabulary

1 Match the words from the text with their meanings a–g.

1 ☐ date (line 6)
2 ☐ impress (line 6)
3 ☐ hooked (line 12)
4 ☐ choke (line 19)
5 ☐ inhale (line 19)
6 ☐ spit (line 19)
7 ☐ aware (line 33)

a very keen on sth (informal)
b make sb respect and admire you because of sth you have said or done
c breathe in deeply
d meeting with a person of the opposite sex
e be unable to breathe because the air passage to the lungs is blocked
f conscious of; realizing
g force liquid, food, etc. out of one's mouth

2 Complete the sentences with one of the words above in an appropriate form.

1 Gary .... on a fish bone.
2 Nigel wasn't .... that the police car was following him until they put on their siren.
3 Babies .... food out if they don't like it.
4 I thought fishing would be boring but when I caught my first trout, I was ....
5 I hate .... other people's cigarette smoke.
6 I didn't know you were such a good cook. This is delicious. I'm ....
7 I can't see you tonight. I've got a .... with my boyfriend.

Understanding the text

1 Why do you think Steve waited until their second date before he took her to see the volcano?

....

2 What is the effect of using the words *breathing*, *choking*, and *inhaling* to describe the erupting volcano?

....

3 *'I'd rather have ten minutes of something wonderful than a lifetime of nothing special, wouldn't you?'* What does this comment tell us about Donna?

....

Lava erupting from Kilauea volcano in Hawaii.

Vocabulary

Topic vocabulary: geographical features

1 Match the words below with the numbered features in the drawings.

bay	beach	cliff	estuary
field	forest	harbour	hill
lake	meadow	mountain	
path	peak	river	rocks
shore	stream	valley	
waterfall	wood		

2 Complete the sentences with one of the adjectives below. Use each adjective once only.

deep	fast-flowing	fertile
mountainous	pebbly	rocky
shallow	steep	

1 The area is ....; some of the peaks are over 3,000m high.

2 The walk along the cliff top is dangerous. The cliffs are .... at this point and the path is ....

3 The water is .... near the shore, but quite .... in the middle of the lake.

4 Because the beach in Brighton is ...., it is unpleasant to walk on.

5 At the foot of the mountains there is a .... valley through which the .... River Avon runs.

Topic vocabulary: sounds people make

1 Match the verbs in italics in sentences 1–6 with their definitions a–f.

1 ☐ When the singer walked onto the stage all the girls in the audience *screamed*.

2 ☐ The little girl *sobbed* uncontrollably when she broke her favourite doll.

3 ☐ 'I've won! I've won!' she *gasped* in amazement.

4 ☐ 'Oh, no! I'll have to start all over again,' he *groaned*.

5 ☐ The bar was so noisy I had to *yell* to make myself heard.

6 ☐ Darren *sighed* with relief when he opened the letter and saw that he had passed.

a make a long, deep sound of pain, disappointment, unhappiness

b take a long, deep, audible breath when you are sad, relieved, tired

c give a long, high-pitched shout of fear, pain, or excitement

d take one or more quick, deep breaths because of surprise, pain, or lack of air

e cry noisily taking in deep breaths

f shout loudly

2 What sound might you make in the following situations? There may be more than one possibility.

1 Your boss tells you that you have to work next weekend. ....

2 You see a mouse. (You are terrified of mice.) ....

3 You have been running for the last ten minutes. (You are not very fit.) ....

4 You see someone trying to break into your car. ....

5 You have just received some very upsetting news. ....

6 It's raining and you wanted to play tennis. ....

7 Someone has just punched you in the stomach. ....

8 You think you have just seen a ghost. ....

Word-building: -able

The suffix -able combines with verbs to form adjectives.
For example, something you can predict is *predictable*.

1 Complete the sentences with an appropriate adjective formed from one of the verbs. You will sometimes need to use a negative form.

| accept | enjoy | predict | prefer | profit | recognize | rely | wash |

1 Take care when climbing in the mountains. Even in summer the weather is very ....

2 The Lada might not be the most exciting car in the world but it is very .... It never breaks down.

3 John was almost .... He looks so different with a beard.

4 Eating out is .... to eating at home because there's no washing-up.

5 Ellen was fired because the way she treated the customers was .... She was extremely rude to them.

6 Luke runs a .... business. That's why he can afford to buy a Ferrari.

7 The blouse wasn't .... so I had to take it to the dry-cleaner's.

8 The evening was very .... We went to the cinema and then had a meal.

2 Mark the stress on the verbs and on the adjectives. On which adjective is the stress different?

Phrasal verbs: *fall* + particle

1 Match the phrasal verbs with their definitions. Use the example sentences 1–5 to help you.

fall back on	stop being friends with sb
fall behind	(of an arrangement or plan) fail to happen
fall for	use for help because no other alternative is available
fall out	fail to do sth quickly enough or on time
fall through	be strongly attracted to sb

1 If I lose my job I'll just have to *fall back on* my savings.
2 I'm worried about Anna. She *is falling behind* with her school work.
3 I think Robert *has fallen for* Mandy. He can't take his eyes off her.
4 Dave and Alex must have *fallen out*. They're obviously not speaking to each other.
5 I thought I had found a buyer for my car but then it all *fell through*.

2 Check your answers. Then decide if the phrasal verbs in the following sentences are correct. Correct any wrong sentences.

1 Tony and Patricia *fell back on* each other the moment they met.
2 They have taken away my television because I *fell through* with the payments on it.
3 I've got a supply of candles to *fall for* if the electricity fails.
4 They had a silly argument and *fell out*. They still haven't made up.
5 We were planning to go to Florida on holiday but it all *fell behind* when Steve lost his job.

Grammar

1 Causatives review

1 Complete the sentences with the structure *have / get* + object + past participle of the verb in brackets. Use both forms where both are possible.

1 I really must *get (have)* my eyes *tested* .... !

2 ' .... your boots ....
(mend)!' yelled the Sergeant Major.

3 I .... this skirt ....
(shorten) last week. What do you think?

4 I really must .... my grey suit
.... (dry-clean) before Jason's wedding.

5 When was the last time you ....
it .... (clean)?

6 She .... her hair ....
(tint). That's not its natural colour.

7 Why don't you .... the house
.... (decorate)? It'll make it easier to sell.

8 I .... the windows ....
(clean) yesterday. Can't you tell?

9 Sarah's mother was going to make the wedding cake but she was ill so they
.... it .... (make) by a local baker.

10 In Britain if you are under 16 you need your parents' permission if you want ....
your ears .... (pierce).

11 We've got lots of plans. We are going to
.... the small bedroom
.... (convert) into a bathroom and we are going to .... a shower
.... (install).

2 Rewrite these jumbled sentences.

1 you your had cut have hair?

....

2 next alarm getting a we fitted are week burglar

....

3 house have painted we blue might the

....

4 fixed had Michael yet car his has?

....

5 usually get teeth I every my months polished six

....

2 Causative verbs

1 Complete the sentences by adding an appropriate past participle formed from the verbs below.

| break | break into | burgle | let down |
| scratch | smash | steal | take |

1 Ben's car was .... last night.
2 His car radio was ....
3 The paintwork was ....
4 The aerial was ....
5 His tyres were ....
6 His windscreen was ....
7 Natalie's flat has been .... three times this year.
8 The video has been .... each time.

2 Check your answers. Then rewrite the passive sentences above using the structure *have* + object + past participle.

1 *Ben had his car broken into last night.* ....
2 ....
3 ....
4 ....
5 ....
6 ....
7 ....
8 ....

3 Question tags

Write in the missing question tags.

1 Lisa wasn't born in Australia, ... ?
2 She lives in Australia now, ... ?
3 She'd rather live in Australia than England, ... ?
4 The winters aren't as severe there, ... ?
5 Sydney isn't the capital of Australia, ... ?
6 It's Canberra that's the capital, ... ?
7 Lisa used to be keen on swimming, ... ?
8 She's never liked football though, ... ?
9 Australians say 'G-day' instead of 'Hello', ... ?
10 There are a lot of kangaroos in Australia, ... ?
11 Nothing happened, ... ?
12 Open the window, ... ?
13 Let's finish this tomorrow, ... ?
14 Robert didn't reply, ... ?
15 Simon went home early, ... ?
16 Nobody else is coming, ... ?
17 Don't ever do that again, ... ?
18 Somebody knows where my pencil is, ... ?
19 Let's open the champagne now, ... ?
20 Nothing has changed, ... ?

Question tags and requests

Make the requests sound less formal by using question tags.

1 Could you lend me £5?

You couldn't lend me £5, could you? ....

2 Do you mind if I leave now?

You don't mind if I leave now, do you? ....

3 Do you mind if I open the window?

....

4 Can you give me a lift?

....

5 Do you mind if I'm a bit late?

....

6 Could you post this letter for me?

....

Writing

Connecting ideas (4)

1 You are going to read a short text about the advantages of living in a city. First write down three advantages you think the writer will include.

....

....

....

2 Read the text through quickly. Are the three main advantages the writer mentions the same as yours?

> **It seems to be unfashionable these days to admit to enjoying living in a city. By all accounts, cities are dirty, polluted, over-crowded, unfriendly, crime-ridden places. Who, given a choice, would rather live in a city than in the country? Well I, for one, would.**
>
> <u>In the first place</u>, cities are exciting places, especially at night. Samuel Johnson said, 'If you are tired of London, you are tired of life'. This is true. But not only of London. The same applies to any big city. In cities there is always something to do, something to see. You need never be bored in a city.
>
> Then there is the convenience of living in a city. If you want to go shopping or go out for the evening, it couldn't be easier. The shops, cinemas, theatres, and restaurants are all on your doorstep.
>
> Finally, and most importantly, if you live near your workplace you will save time on travel. You will not have to spend an hour or more commuting to and from work every day. You will be able to spend the time that you save more profitably and pleasurably – enjoying all the attractions the city has to offer.

3 The writer uses certain words and phrases to order his ideas, for example, *In the first place*. Find two more examples of similar words or expressions in the text and underline them. What do you notice about their position in the sentence and in the text?

4 The following words and phrase could be used to replace the three you underlined. Write them next to the one they could replace.

Secondly (Thirdly, etc.)   Lastly   To begin with; Firstly

5 You are going to write a short article about either the advantages or the disadvantages of one of the following.
   * living in a particular place (the country, a village, etc.)
   * a particular hobby or sport
   * living alone (or living with friends or one's parents)
   * being single (or being married)
   * a particular job

1 Before you start, think of three advantages or disadvantages and put them in order of importance.

2 Write your main ideas in topic sentences. Then write one or more ideas to support each topic sentence. These can be examples or more detailed information.

3 Think of an idea for your opening paragraph. This should hold the reader's attention and make them want to read on. It could be:
   * an interesting statement or question
     (*Who in their right mind would prefer to live in the city than in the country? Apparently, more and more people are choosing city life above country life. There are obvious advantages.*)
   * a general opinion
     (*Most people think that stamp-collecting is a boring hobby, something that only nine-year-old boys do. I would disagree with them and argue that stamp-collecting is a fascinating hobby, of interest to people of all ages.*)

4 Write out your article in paragraphs. Remember to use an ordering word or phrase before each new point.

5 When you have finished, read through what you have written. Are your arguments clear? Is your article interesting?

6 When you are satisfied with what you have written, write out your final version, correcting any mistakes in spelling, grammar, and punctuation.

Reading

Before you read

You are going to read an article about the importance of body language and appearance to police officers, customs officers, and job interviewers. First, decide whether these statements are True or False.

1 ☐ Our body language (the way we communicate our thoughts and feelings with our bodies rather than with words) is of equal importance to all three groups.

2 ☐ You would probably be stopped by a police officer if you looked nervous and guilty.

3 ☐ Most criminals are male and under twenty.

4 ☐ If you don't want to be stopped by customs officials, walk quickly past them looking confident.

5 ☐ What we say at a job interview is more important than how we say it.

6 ☐ When people lie, they exaggerate their body language.

As you read

Check your answers. Correct any wrong statements.

Glossary

size sb up (headline): form an opinion of sb
nervous wreck (line 1): state of extreme nervous tension
jaywalking (line 4): walking slowly along or across a street without paying attention to the traffic
non-verbal (line 8): without speaking
psychological profile (line 15): description of the likely character, behaviour, and interests of a criminal based on information about the crime they have committed
Customs and Excise (line 24): government department that collects taxes on goods brought in from other countries
hard and fast (line 26): fixed and unable to be changed
Nothing to Declare (line 32): exit sb passes through if they are not carrying goods on which they need to pay tax
bravado (line 34): behaving in an over-confident way
braided (line 37): (of hair) worn in plaits
prejudice (line 48): dislike of a person, group, or culture based on feeling not rational thought
count for a lot (line 49): be of great importance

What are they looking at?

Police officer

1 Some people turn into nervous wrecks simply by walking past a police officer. They may be guilty of nothing more than jaywalking back in 1992, but their body
5 language still screams 'Arrest me!'

2 If you fall into this category it's not all bad news. The police officer isn't paying attention to your non-verbal communication. In fact, they're trained
10 not to.

3 'Police officers are told not to judge somebody by their appearance,' says a City of London Police spokesman. 'What is relevant is whether they're breaking the law or not.'

4 However, the British police are making increasing use of
15 psychological profiles of different criminal types. It's well known that the majority of crimes are committed by males under 20, but you're also more likely to be an offender if you have a short, muscular build and tattoos.

5 One area of police work where non-verbal communication
20 is of vital importance is the interview room. Sadly, the police were unwilling to share their body language tips with us.

Focus on vocabulary

1 Find words or phrases in the article with the meanings below. The paragraph numbers are given in brackets.

Police officer

1 form an opinion about sb or sth (3) ....

2 essential (5) ....

3 not prepared (to do sth) (5) ....

4 small, useful pieces of practical advice (5) ....

Customs officer

1 person who speaks on behalf of a group (6) ....

2 choose sb from a group for special attention (7) ....

3 people who take goods or people into or out of a country illegally (8) ....

4 direct one's attention to (9) ....

Job interviewer

1 ideas, feelings, or opinions formed immediately without conscious thought (10) ....

2 general; taking everything into account (11) ....

3 make sth seem larger, better, worse, etc. than it really is (12)

....

4 not moving (12) ....

A guide to what professional interrogators are looking for when they size you up.

Customs officer

6 'Anyone can be stopped and checked by Customs and Excise
25 officials,' explains a spokesperson. 'There are no hard and fast rules. We've stopped people dressed as nuns before. Any sign of fear is one thing we do look out for.'

7   This might involve singling out people who walk through the Nothing to Declare door a little too quickly, sweat heavily, or avoid eye-contact. However, self-conscious bravado may also attract attention.

8   Looking unusual can also lead to problems for smugglers. 'Two years ago a woman came into Gatwick with very striking braided hair. A female Customs officer thought there was something odd about it, and took her to one side. It turned out that she had
40 hundreds of grammes of cocaine hidden in the braids.'

9   However, where you've come from is as important as the way you walk. 'We do target certain routes. We don't check flights from Japan as often as ones from Amsterdam.'

Job interviewer

10 'First impressions come across in five seconds,' according to a personnel adviser. 'Most of the information taken in then is based on people's prejudices which, unfortunately, count for a lot.'

11   Apparently, words contribute to only about seven per cent of the overall impression a person communicates. Tone of voice makes up 38% and the rest is non-verbal –
55 body language, clothes, and facial expressions.

12   'You would look for the signs that someone was lying: perhaps they are touching their face or nose, or they may avoid eye-contact and fiddle with a collar or tie. When people are lying, they will sometimes
60 exaggerate their body language. On the other hand, they may try to hide it and be too static. The trouble is these things could just be symptoms of nerves!

13   'I've even heard of really strange interviews where the interviewer lies on the floor behind the desk to see how
65 the person reacts. The one who gets the job comes along and does the same thing.'

— *Focus* magazine —

---

2 **Check your answers. Then complete the sentences with one of the words or phrases you found in an appropriate form.**

1 A .... for the government has denied that there will be a rise in taxes.

2 The .... were caught with 20 kilos of heroin hidden in the boot of their car.

3 The saying 'You can't .... a book by its cover' is quite true.

4 Stop ....! The exam was difficult, but not that difficult!

5 What was your .... of Kate's new boyfriend?

6 It is .... that you rest after a major operation.

7 Although the skater fell once, her .... performance was good.

8 Julie gave me a good .... for getting chewing gum off clothes.

9 Dave doesn't like people to know his private affairs and was .... to tell us how much he earned.

10 Nowadays more and more advertising campaigns .... young people.

11 It wouldn't be fair to .... anyone in particular. Everyone has contributed to the success of the project.

12 House prices, which have been .... for months, are rising again.

Understanding the text

1 'Their body language screams "Arrest me!"' What information does their body language give the police officer?

....

2 Why do you think the writer says '*Sadly* the police were unwilling to share their body language tips with us.'

....

3 Why might a smuggler pass through customs dressed as a nun?

....

4 According to the information given in the article, why is it important to look smart at a job interview?

....

5 What kind of person do you think the interviewer who lay on the floor was looking for? What advantage would such an unconventional interview technique have over more conventional techniques?

....

Vocabulary

Topic vocabulary: the body

Collocations

1 Match one of the verbs in A
with one of the nouns in B.

	A	B
1 ☐	bite	a shoulders
2 ☐	blow	b eyebrows
3 ☐	clap	c head
4 ☑ *g*	clear	d head
5 ☐	cross	e legs
6 ☐	nod	f hands
7 ☐	raise	g throat
8 ☐	shake	h nose
9 ☐	shrug	i nails

2 Complete the sentences with one of the verb + noun combinations.
Add any other necessary words.

1 To show approval of something you can *clap your hands.*

2 When someone has a cold they often ....

3 To show that you agree you may ....

4 Before you say something important you might ....

5 When people are relaxed they may ....

6 To say 'No' you can simply ....

7 When people are surprised or disapprove they often ....

8 When you don't know or don't care you might ....

9 When some people are nervous they ....

Phrasal verbs: three-part verbs

1 Replace the verbs in italics in the sentences with one of the three-part phrasal verbs
in an appropriate form. Use a dictionary if necessary.

catch up on	face up to	go along with	go down with	look up to

1 Daniel *has caught* a viral infection.
2 Amanda can't *accept* the fact that Ian doesn't love her any more.
3 I *agree with* what you say.
4 Come over tomorrow and we can *find out* each other's news.
5 Rachel *admires and respects* her elder brother.

2 Complete the sentences with a three-part verb from the list above in an appropriate
form.

1 Let's meet soon. I can't wait .... all the gossip.
2 I'm sorry but I can't .... your views at all. In fact, I strongly disagree.
3 He's a well-respected member of the community; everyone .... him.
4 Jess can't come. She .... a terrible cold.
5 Lauren finds it hard .... her responsibilities.

Word-building

Complete the sentences with the correct form of the word in bold.

appear

1 The .... of the young child caused a lot of anxiety.

2 The beard really changes John's ....

impress

3 I think I made a good .... at the interview.

4 The candidate's qualifications were very ....

5 Real Madrid won the match .... by five goals to nil.

communicate

6 We can learn a lot about a person through non-verbal ....

7 Peter isn't very ...., is he?

offend

8 Most .... are young adult males.

9 It is an .... to park on double yellow lines.

increase

10 Customs officials are making .... use of sniffer dogs.

11 It is becoming .... difficult to get a job.

will

12 The woman was .... to say who had given her the package.

13 As he didn't have anything to hide, he opened his suitcase ....

attract

14 Buckingham Palace is one of London's main tourist ....

15 Most film stars are physically ....

Grammar

1 Reported speech review

1 Rewrite the dialogue between Sally and Amy in reported speech. Use the verbs *ask* or *say*.

1 Sally: 'Have you applied for any jobs, Amy?'
Sally asked Amy if she had applied for any jobs.

2 Sally: 'How many job applications have you sent off, Amy?'
....

3 Amy: 'I've sent off ten. I've got an interview tomorrow.'
....

4 Sally: 'What are you going to wear?'
....

5 Amy: 'I think I'll wear my navy suit. Could I borrow your white blouse?'
....

6 Sally: 'It's at the dry-cleaner's. Will you take the job if they offer it to you?'
....

7 Amy: 'I probably will if they offer me a decent salary.'
....

2 Rewrite the reported speech sentences in direct speech.

1 Sally asked Amy if she had had the interview.
'Have you had the interview, Amy?' Sally asked.

2 Sally asked Amy how the interview had gone.
....

3 Amy replied that she had been very nervous.
....

4 Amy told Sally that she didn't think she would get the job because they wanted someone who could speak Spanish.
....

5 Sally asked Amy whether she would be disappointed if she didn't get the job.
....

6 Amy replied that she had an interview for a job in London the following week, which she was more interested in.
....

2 Reporting verbs

1 Rewrite the direct speech sentences in reported speech using the verb given.

1 'I'll be home late,' he announced.
He announced that he would be home late.

2 'Don't take anything into the UK that you shouldn't,' my friend advised before I left for the airport.

3 'Don't try to take any extra alcohol or cigarettes,' he warned. 'The customs officers at Heathrow are very strict.'

4 'It's not worth the risk,' he insisted. 'You could be sent to prison.'

5 'I'll risk taking an extra carton of cigarettes,' I decided.

6 'Have you anything to declare?' the Customs officer asked.

7 'Could you open your case, please?' he asked.

8 'Open that carrier bag, too!' he instructed.

9 'I didn't know I could only bring in one carton of cigarettes,' I argued.

10 'It was stupid of me not to check,' I admitted.

11 'Come with me,' the Customs officer ordered.

2 Some friends are trying to decide what to buy Katie for her birthday. Report each suggestion in a different way.

1 'We could buy Katie a book for her birthday,' Keith suggested.

2 'How about getting her a CD?' Karen said.

3 'Why don't we ask her what she wants?' David said.

3 Infinitives or gerunds after verbs

Choose the correct verb form in these sentences.
If both forms are possible underline both options.

1 I can't help *to like / liking* him even though he's unreliable.
2 I expect *to get / getting* a pay rise next month.
3 I pretended *to agree / agreeing* with him.
4 I learnt *to type / typing* when I was at school.
5 I hate *to admit / admitting* it but I enjoy *to work / working*.
6 I've decided *to take / taking* early retirement.
7 I'm going to put off *to take / taking* a decision until I have to.
8 I refuse *to work / working* overtime unless I get double pay.
9 My job prevents me *to have / having* a normal family life.
10 We hope *to reach / reaching* an agreement soon.
11 My neighbour continued *to work / working* after he won the lottery.
12 We start *to work / working* at 9 o'clock.
13 I intend *to ask / asking* for some time off.
14 She chose *to ignore / ignoring* my advice.

Infinitives and gerunds with a change of meaning

Choose the correct alternative form, the infinitive or the gerund.

1 I'll never forget *to get / getting* my first pay cheque.
2 James went on *to play / playing* after the others had stopped.
3 I meant *to remind / reminding* you but I forgot.
4 I don't remember *to tell / telling* you that. Are you sure I did?
5 I've stopped *to go / going* to the gym. I got fed up.
6 I've been trying *to explain / explaining* but you wouldn't listen.
7 I forgot *to tell / telling* Dean I'd be home late.
8 I'm going to get what I want even if it means *to tell / telling* a lie.
9 I remembered *to send / sending* Paula a birthday card. I forgot last year.
10 Do you regret *to marry / marrying* so young?
11 Sorry we're a bit late. We stopped *to have / having* a drink at Charlie's.
12 Have you tried *to eat / eating* apple pie with cheese? It's delicious.

Writing

Register

1 Read the three texts which are all connected with a job interview. Decide who they have been written to and from, and whether each text is written in formal or informal language.

> 1 Ms Mayall is a well-qualified candidate with a degree in French and Spanish from Birmingham University. She also has a diploma in secretarial studies and good word-processing skills. Ms Mayall is presently working as a personal assistant to the managing director of Lambert Electronics, where she has worked for the last five years. Ms Mayall said that she enjoyed working at Lambert but that she would like the opportunity to use her languages. Her present employers have provided her with excellent references. At the interview she was confident and well-spoken. I would recommend that this candidate be short-listed for the above post.

> 2 ... so busy with interviews all week. I thought we'd never find the right person to take over June Marshall's job (you remember June, don't you?) but we interviewed someone today that I'm sure would be perfect. She's got the right background and although she's been working for a much smaller company, I'm sure she ...

> 3 The interview went quite well I think. But you never really know, do you? There were two other applicants – both a bit older than me. Neither of them had Spanish though. I'd really like the job 'cos they're expanding into Europe so I'd get a chance to use my languages. Better late than never!!! Anyway, fingers crossed. See you soon.

2 Check your answers. Then find four examples of features of informal language and three of formal language.

Informal language

1 Short sentences   The interview went quite well, I think.
2 ....
3 ....
4 ....

Formal language

1 ....
2 ....
3 ....

3 Read the formal letter asking someone to attend a job interview. Choose the appropriate formal alternative.

> *Thank you/Thanks*[1] for your letter of application for the *job/post*[2] of assistant to the managing director. We *want/would like*[3] you to *attend/come for*[4] an interview on Friday 19th October at 11 a.m. Please *make sure/ensure*[5] that we *get/receive*[6] a reference from your present *employer/boss*[7] and one other reference before *you come/that date*[8]. Please *advise us/let us know*[9] if the time and date are not convenient. *See you on the 19th./ We look forward to seeing you on the 19th*[10].

4 Read the informal written request for a reference. Choose the most appropriate phrase from a-e below for each gap.

> Dear Sarah, ...[1] I hate having to ask you but ....[2] another reference? ....[3] next Friday and ....[4] before then. ....[5]   Angie

a I am sorry that I have not written for such a long time. / It's been ages since I've written, I know. Sorry!
b do you think you could write me / would it be at all possible for you to write me
c I've got an interview / I've been called for an interview
d it's essential that they receive my references / they want my references in
e I'm very grateful. / Thanks a million.

5 You are going to do two short pieces of writing.
  • A formal report on Angela Mitchell by a person who interviewed her, who was not very impressed.
  • A letter from Angela to a friend telling them what went wrong at the interview, and why she thinks she won't get the job.

1 Use these notes and the model texts to help you. Add your own ideas.

> **Post: Assistant to Managing Director**
> **Name:** Angela Mitchell
> **Qualifications:** Diploma in secretarial studies and word-processing.
> **Experience:** Office typist since left school 10 years ago. Has worked for five different companies!
> **References:** Good (reliable and hard-working)
> **Comments:** Smart appearance; didn't ask many questions; some French; doesn't seem very ambitious. Not enough experience for this position.

2 Write out a rough draft for each piece of writing. Use appropriate formal or informal language.

3 Read through your first version, correcting any mistakes. Does the report sound impersonal and the letter friendly?

4 When you are satisfied, write out your final version.

Phrasal verbs

A phrasal verb is a verb used with a particle (an adverb or preposition). Some phrasal verbs are idiomatic. The meaning of the verb and particle together is something different from the separate literal meanings of the verb and the particle. Phrasal verbs are very common in English, especially in informal English.

In addition to learning the meaning of phrasal verbs, you also need to know how to use them correctly and, most importantly, whether the verb and particle have to stay together or whether they can be separated.

The grammar of phrasal verbs

There are four main types of phrasal verb.

Type 1	verb + particle (no object)
	Examples **break down** **get by**

Phrasal verbs like these are always inseparable – the verb and the adverb always stay together and can never be separated by other words.

> *My car **broke down** on my way to work.*
> *We **get by** as well as we can.*

These are intransitive verbs. They cannot take an object.

Type 2	verb + particle + object / verb + object + particle
	Examples **throw away** **get across**

Phrasal verbs like these are separable – the object of the verb can come between the verb and the adverb. If the object is a noun, it can come before or after the particle.

> *She **threw away** the rubbish.*
> *She **threw** the rubbish **away**.*

If the object is a pronoun, it **must** come between the verb and the particle.

> *She **threw** it **away**.*   NOT *She threw away it.*

These are transitive verbs. They take an object.

Type 3	verb + particle + object
	Examples **make for** **get round**

Phrasal verbs like these are inseparable – the object of the verb cannot come between the verb and the preposition.

> *He opened the door and **made for** the kitchen.*
> *She could always **get round** her father.*

This rule is still true when the object is a pronoun.

> *You won't **get round** me!*

Type 4	verb + particle + particle + object
	Examples **look up to** **catch up on**

Phrasal verbs like these are inseparable – the three parts of the verb always stay together, whether the object is a noun or a pronoun.

> *She **looks up to** her brother.*
> *I **caught up on** her news.*

Meanings

Some phrasal verbs can have more than one meaning, for example **break down**.

> *My car **broke down** on the motorway.*
> (= stopped working)
> *She **broke down** when she heard the news.*
> (= collapsed in tears)

They can also be more than one type, for example **get over**.

> *I knew what I wanted to say but I couldn't **get** it **over** to anyone else.* [Type 2]
> *It took her several weeks to **get over** her illness.* [Type 3]

This is because the particle **over** can be either an adverb or a preposition.

Dictionaries

When you want to check the meaning of a phrasal verb, use your dictionary. Most dictionaries list phrasal verbs at the end of the entry for the main verb. The phrasal verbs are listed in the order of the particles following them. For example, in the *Oxford Advanced Learner's Dictionary*, the phrasal verbs are clearly listed in a section marked **PHR V**. The different meanings of each phrasal verb are listed and an example is given.

> **set off** to begin a journey: *What time are you planning to set off tomorrow?* ∘ *They've set off on a trip around the world.* ∘ *We set off for London just after 10 o'clock.* **set sth off 1** to make a bomb, etc explode: *A gang of boys were setting off fireworks in the street.* **2** to make an alarm start ringing: *If you open this door, it will set off the alarm.*

It is easy to check which type a phrasal verb is in the dictionary:

Type 1 verbs are written **without sb** and **sth**, for example *set off*. When you see this you know that these verbs do not take an object.

Type 2 verbs are written with *sb/sth* **between** the verb and the particle, for example *set sth off*. When you see *sb* or *sth* between the two parts of the phrasal verb you know that they can be separated by an object.

Type 3 phrasal verbs are written with *sb/sth* **after** the particle, for example *come across sth*. When you see *sb* or *sth* after the two parts of the phrasal verb you know that it cannot be separated by an object.

Type 4 verbs are written with *sb/sth* **after** the two particles, for example *look up to sb/sth*. When you see *sb* or *sth* after the three parts of the phrasal verb you know that they cannot be separated by an object.

This list includes all the phrasal verbs which appear in the Vocabulary sections of this Workbook. The unit number is given, and the number in square brackets tells you what type of phrasal verb it is. Some Type 1 verbs can be used with a second particle, as a Type 4 verb. The second particle is given in brackets in the list.

break down (unit 6): (of a machine) stop working [1]
break down (unit 6): collapse in tears [1]
break up (unit 1): (for schools, etc.) begin the holidays [1]
break up (unit 1): divide or become divided into smaller parts [1]
break up/break sth up (unit 1): end a relationship [1/2]
bring sth about (unit 3): cause to happen [2]
bring sth down (unit 3): lower or reduce sth [2]
bring sth in (unit 3): introduce new laws, rules, etc. [2]
bring sth out (unit 3): produce and sell a new product [2]
bring sb together (unit 3): unite in one place [2]
bring sth up (unit 6): introduce a subject into the conversation [2]
bring sb up (unit 6): look after a child until it is an adult [2]
catch up on sth (unit 12): spend time doing sth you have not had time to do [4]
come across sth (unit 7): find accidentally [3]
come off (unit 2): (infml) be successful [1]
come off sth (unit 2): originate from a place or thing [3]
come out (unit 7): be revealed or made public [1]
come round (unit 7): regain consciousness [1]
come round (unit 7): visit [1]
come up (unit 7): happen unexpectedly [1]
come up against sth (unit 7): be faced with a problem or difficulty [4]
come up with sth (unit 7): think of a plan or solution [4]
face up to sth (unit 12): accept and deal with a difficult situation [4]
fall back on sth (unit 11): use for help because no other alternative is available [4]
fall behind (with sth) (unit 11): fail to do sth quickly enough or on time [1]
fall for sb (unit 11): be strongly attracted to sb [3]
fall out (with sb) (unit 11): stop being friends (with sb) [1]
fall through (unit 11): (of an arrangement or plan) fail to happen [1]
get sth across (unit 5): communicate an idea to others [2]
get away (from sth) (unit 2): escape [1]
get away (unit 2): have a holiday [1]
get by (on sth) (unit 5): manage [1]
*****get sb down** (unit 5): depress [2]
get out of sth (unit 5): avoid doing sth [4]
get over sth (unit 5): recover from an illness or shock [3]
get round sb (unit 5): persuade sb to let you do or have sth [3]
get round to sth (unit 5): do sth after a long delay [4]
get through sth (unit 5): consume [3]
give sth away (unit 4): accidentally reveal information [2]
give sth away (unit 4): give without taking money in return [2]
go along with sth (unit 12): agree with and accept an idea [4]

go away (unit 4): disappear [1]
go away (unit 4): leave home for a time, especially on holiday [1]
go down with sth (unit 12): catch and develop an illness [4]
look up to sb (unit 12): respect and admire sb [4]
make for sth (unit 8): move, usually rather hurriedly, towards a particular place [3]
make for sth (unit 8): provide [3]
make sth out (unit 8): manage to see, read or hear sth [2]
make sth out (unit 8): write out a bill, etc. [2]
make sth up (unit 6/8): invent an excuse, story, etc. [2]
make up (with sb) (unit 6/8): forgive and become friends again after an argument [1]
make sth up (unit 8): (usually passive) consist of; comprise [2]
make up for sth (unit 8): compensate [4]
pull out (of sth) (unit 9): decide not to continue an activity [1]
pull out (unit 9): leave [1]
pull sth out (unit 9): remove [2]
put sth away (unit 4): put sth tidily in its place [2]
put sth away (unit 4): save money [2]
put sth off (unit 9): delay or postpone [2]
put sth off (unit 9): extinguish a light, etc. [2]
put sb off (unit 9): make sb lose interest in sth [2]
put sb off (unit 9): make sb lose their concentration [2]
set sth off (unit 1): make an alarm ring [2]
set sth off (unit 1): make sth explode [2]
set off (for a place) (unit 1): start a journey [1]
take sth away (unit 4): take sth from sb [2]
take sth away (unit 4): remove sth to another place [2]
take sb in (unit 10): allow sb to live in your house as a favour or as a paying guest [2]
take sb in (unit 10): deceive [2]
take sth in (unit 10): go to see a film, museum, etc. when you are visiting a place [2]
take sth in (unit 10): understand or remember sth you have heard, seen or read [2]
take sth over (unit 2): assume responsibility for a job/task [2]
take sth over (unit 2): buy or gain control of a business [2]
take sth up (unit 6): fill space or time [2]
take sth up (unit 6): start a new job or activity [2]
throw sth away (unit 4): get rid of sth you don't want [2]
throw sth away (unit 4): lose an opportunity or waste a possibility [2]
turn up (unit 1): arrive [1]
turn up (unit 1): be found (after being lost) [1]
turn sth up (unit 1): increase the volume [2]
work out (unit 10): do physical exercise in order to be fit and strong [1]
work sth out (unit 10): find a solution to a problem [2]
work out (unit 10): happen and develop in a satisfactory way [1]

*****get down** is always separable, whether the object is a noun or a pronoun. So you say *It got her down. / It got Louise down.* NOT *It got down Louise.*

Answer key

Unit 1

Reading

Before you read

1 Personal answers

2 1 c 2 b 3 a 4 d 5 e

As you read

1 The only word not in the article is *hospital*.

2 1 It tells us that Andrew and Michael were adventurous. They weren't worried about any possible danger.

2 The fact that the guide was passionate about rafting was reassuring. Michael and Andrew would suppose from this that he was an expert, which gave them confidence in putting themselves in his charge.

3 They probably had absolutely no experience of rafting. Things might be more likely to go wrong because of everyone's inexperience.

4 The guide's instructions were 'frantic' possibly because the rafters weren't reacting to his instructions quickly enough or because they were doing the opposite to what he wanted them to do at a particular time.

5 The expression means that you are soaked in water and being spun round.

6 The word *incredibly* tells us that the writer expected the raft to sink and was amazed that it didn't.

7 The writer is saying that the English don't usually show their emotions because they are reserved.

8 This could have two different meanings depending on whether the words were Scott's or the rafters'. If the words were Scott's, it could mean that he thought they were competent enough to go on to a more difficult rapid. If the words were the rafters', it could mean that they were keen to try something more challenging.

9 The writer was surprised to see Andrew appear on the other side because the guide had warned them that if they went to the right they might drown. Andrew had done this and had survived.

10 The writer enjoyed the experience very much.

Comprehension

1 *obsessive*: lived and breathed rafting (line 20)
untidy and *competent*: chaotic appearance; knew what he was doing (line 27)
relaxed: His roll up was still dry (line 47)

2 a paragraph 10
b paragraph 4
c paragraph 8
d paragraph 7

Focus on vocabulary

2 When Peter saw the bull coming towards him he ran *like crazy*.

3 Andrew's uncle is *in fairly good shape* for a man of seventy.

4 The new boss seems to be quite a nice *chap/guy*.

5 I'll be there in ten minutes *or so*.

6 Julia *turned up* half an hour late as usual.

7 Can I ask you *a couple of* questions?

8 The strong current pulled the swimmer *this way and that*.

9 It was a terrible journey but they finally *made it*.

Vocabulary

Phrasal verbs:
turn up, set off, break up

1 1 d 2 g 3 a 4 f 5 i 6 b 7 h 8 c 9 e

2 1 turn … up
2 break up/broke up
3 turned up
4 broke up
5 set off
6 break … up
7 set off
8 turned up
9 set off

Word groups

1 2 They are all verbs which involve the moving of a person or object. *Pull* means to hold sth firmly and use force in order to move it towards yourself. *Drag* and *haul* mean to pull with effort and difficulty. (Note: *drag* also means to pull sb or sth, not necessarily heavy, along the ground). The odd-one-out is *lift* because it means to move something upwards, and has no sense of difficulty.

3 These are all kinds of boat. The odd-one-out is *liner* because it is a very large ship. The others are much smaller. You *paddle* a canoe and a *raft*; you *row* a rowing boat.

4 These words describe direction or position. The odd-one-out is *upright* because it can only describe position. The others are all used with verbs of movement.

5 These are all actions to do with water. *Swim*, *drift* and *float* are all on the surface of water; *sink* means go down to the bottom of the water. *Drift* is to move without effort in the direction of the current.

2 1 swam 5 haul
2 sank 6 upright
3 sideways 7 dragging
4 canoe

Topic vocabulary: smoking

1 1 light
2 put out/extinguish
3 chain smoker/heavy smoker
4 non-smoker (passive smoking)
5 ashtray
6 filter tip

2 1 heavy smokers
2 non-smokers
3 give up/quit
4 Filter tips
5 passive smoking
6 cut down
7 inhaling
8 addictive
9 ashtrays
10 crave

Grammar

1 Present tenses review

1 More and more people *are taking up* cycling. When we cycle, we *use up* more energy than when we *walk*. Cycling *improves* our aerobic fitness, too.
I *go* cycling regularly, but only on Sundays when the roads are quieter. Then, I *drive* into the country, I *park* the car and I *pedal* up and down tree-lined lanes.
Cycling in towns and cities, however, is another matter. Although some councils *are spending* more money on constructing cycle lanes, cyclists in most towns and cities have to compete for space with lorries and buses. So when you cycle in the city, you *are putting** your life at risk.
**put* is also possible here.

2 1 fly
2 arrive
3 are staying
4 runs
5 fly back
6 am changing
7 am leaving

3 1 eats; consume
2 eat; contain
3 is going up; increases
4 is spending; are taking up
5 is following; goes; cycles; walks

2 Aspect

1 1 c 2 e 3 f 4 d 5 a 6 b

2 1 have started; am eating
2 have read; has tried; am reading
3 is lying; was cooking

3 Action and state verbs

1 1 I'm thinking; do you think;
Don't you realize; don't agree
2 Are you seeing; believes; see
3 are you doing; I'm tasting; tastes;
suppose

2 1 owns; wants; costs; knows
2 do you weigh; prefer
3 do you do; help; Do you have
4 suppose; smells; do you think
5 am having; am thinking

Writing

1 1 Susie Maroney's achievement was
special for two reasons. Swimming
across the Florida Straits is one of the
most difficult swims a swimmer can
attempt because of the tides, currents,
and sharks. She covered the distance 10
hours quicker than expected.

2 **Possible answers**
Not being able to sleep
Having to swim in the cage
The loneliness at night
Being stung by jellyfish
The exhaustion

2 *fed* – given   *stepped* – walked
dragged – pulled   *smeared* – covered

The verbs in italics are more descriptive than
the other verbs so they make the text more
interesting.

3 1 f 2 h 3 c 4 g 5 i 6 e 7 a 8 d 9 b

4 The detail which the adjectives and adverbs
give makes the text come to life.

Unit 2

Reading

Before you read

Possible answers

1 People often go abroad to look for
better job prospects; a better climate; a
better standard of living/lifestyle.

2 They may want to go back home
because they can't find a job; they feel
homesick; they never settle in the
country (perhaps they have language
problems; they are treated as
foreigners); they can't adapt to the
climate; way of life, etc.

3 They may not be able to afford to go
back home (the cost of a ticket; the
expense of starting over again).

As you read

1 Giorgiadis went abroad because he
thought he could make a lot of money
quickly.

2 He wanted to go back to Greece
because he missed Greece, his friends,
and the language.

3 He couldn't sell his business.

Focus on vocabulary

1 1 f 2 g 3 a 4 e 5 b 6 j 7 i 8 c
9 d 10 h

2 1 yard
2 melts/will melt
3 Stools
4 wipe
5 lumpy
6 propped
7 till
8 am longing
9 shade
10 loaded

Comprehension

1 True. He got up at sunset.
2 True. He lifted his *heavy* body.
3 False. His Swahili was *limited*; *a blunt
and imperfect tool.*
4 False. It was the evening.
5 False. It was situated on a busy road
with *endless traffic.*
6 True. He had *the knowledge to run the
business*; he could have a monopoly on
bread for the whole town.
7 True. *Sweated and laboured.*
8 False. He went out after hearing about
other Greeks who had gone there and
how easy it was to make money.
9 False. He had thought of returning to
Greece all the time he was working hard
to establish his business.
10 True. *Bad times to sell.*

Understanding the text

1 Lonely: He doesn't seem to have any
friends. The only people mentioned are
his employees and Mohammed Said,
who is a rival. Unhappy: He spends his
time thinking about his problems and his
profits and dreaming of going home to
Greece, which seems to be an
impossible dream. Monotonous:
Nothing special happened to mark his
day. The passing of time was measured
by the flight of the birds and the ringing
of the cathedral bell.

2 He sleeps in a *lumpy* bed; there is no
bathroom (he washed under a tap in the
yard); there is no gas or electricity (he
sees by means of a kerosene lamp; the
oven is heated by burning wood).

3 They are probably rivals. The text tells us
that Mohammed Said would have the
monopoly on bread if he bought
Giorgiadis's bakery, so Mohammed Said
probably sells bread too.

4 Mohammed Said probably enjoys having
power over Giorgiadis.

Vocabulary

Topic vocabulary:
eating, drinking, talking

1 1   D I S C U S S
2   **S** I P
3   C H E **W**
4   C H **A** T
5   N I B B L **E**
6   G O B B L **E**   U P
7   K N **O** C K   B A C K
           W
8   G O S S I P
9   M U N C H

2 1 chew
2 nibbling
3 knocked back
4 sipped
5 chatted
6 gossip
7 munched
8 discuss
9 gobbled up/down
10 swallow

Phrasal verbs:
get away, come off, take over

1 1 b 2 d 3 f 4 e 5 a 6 c

2 1 got away
2 didn't come off
3 took over
4 get away
5 will/is going to take over
6 come/coming off

3 Personal answers

Collocations: verb + noun

1 **run**   a race   a business
break a record   a promise
take   a day off   turns
        a fool of oneself   a record
make   a promise   fun of someone

2 1 Possible answer: you feel stupid or
embarrassed.

2 An unreliable, insincere or unscrupulous
person breaks promises. The opposite of
to *break* a promise is to *keep* a promise.

3 If you run a business you are the
manager or the managing director of
the company.

4 Possible answer: you could make your
fortune by winning the lottery, writing a
best-seller, inventing or discovering sth
important.

5 If you take turns with your partner or
flatmate to cook the evening meal, you
will cook three or four times a week. It
depends who cooks the first meal.

6 If you run a marathon, you run
approximately 42 kms.

7 Personal answer. You can make fun of
people you like and people you dislike.

Grammar

1 Past simple and Past continuous review

1 played
2 was having
3 was washing up
4 was playing
5 was
6 spotted
7 were lying
8 had
9 decided
10 noticed
11 was chairing
12 bent down
13 laughed
14 pointed out
15 happened
16 threw away
17 cancelled
18 drew

2 Past Perfect

1 had rained; had stopped
2 had planned
3 had shone; had thought
4 had made
5 had dropped
6 had already seen; hadn't liked
7 had gone out; hadn't enjoyed; had turned out

3 *used to, would*

1 Life is quite different from what it *used to be*/~~would be~~ like eighty years ago.
2 Then people *didn't use to have*/~~wouldn't have~~ so much free time.
3 They *used to work*/*would work* a six-day week.
4 Sunday was their only day off, and on Sunday most people *used to go*/*would go* to church.
5 People *used to spend*/*would spend* their summer holiday in their own countries, if they could afford one. Nowadays the most popular holiday destinations are abroad.
6 Before the age of the aeroplane, if you wanted to travel to America from Europe it *used to take*/*would take* up to six weeks to get there.
7 The voyage *used to be*/~~would be~~ hazardous, and some people never arrived.
8 In the past people *didn't use to live*/~~wouldn't live~~ as long as they do now.
9 They *used to die*/*would die* at a much younger age – many from diseases like tuberculosis, which are now curable.
10 All in all, life *used to be*/~~would be~~ much harder.

Past Tenses

1 b	5 c	9 a	13 b
2 a; b	6 b	10 b	14 c
3 a	7 b	11 c	
4 a	8 a	12 b; c	

Writing

Using correct punctuation

1
a 5	d 7	g 2	j 6
b 8	e 3	h 4	
c 1	f 10	i 9	

2
2 exclamation mark
3 full stop
4 inverted commas
5 colon
6 brackets
7 comma
8 question mark
9 apostrophe
10 capital letter

3 I remember it as if it were yesterday, although it happened a long time ago. When I was seven, the doctor decided that my tonsils should be removed, which meant a small operation and a short stay in hospital.

My parents took me there in the afternoon and left me. It was the first time I had been separated from my parents; I was devastated. I remember that, for some reason, my bed was in the centre of the ward so I felt that everyone was staring at me and cried myself to sleep that night.

The next morning I woke up in a different bed, next to an old lady. My throat hurt and I didn't know where I was. I remember a nurse saying, 'I'm sure you'd like some ice-cream, wouldn't you? It's good for you!' I was not convinced and refused to eat it.

That was my first time in hospital, and the experience was so traumatic that I have had a horror of hospitals ever since. Just the smell of disinfectant is enough to bring it all back.

Unit 3

Reading

As you read

1 Beaches will be smaller.
2 Fewer people will go to Mediterranean resorts on holiday.
3 Temperatures will rise by up to 4°C.
4 There will be less rain in south-east Spain.
5 Sea levels will rise.
6 Deserts will get bigger.
7 North Africa will have water shortages.
8 Some Mediterranean countries will not be able to grow cereals.
9 Diseases like malaria will increase.

Understanding the text

1 They will probably have many more important problems to deal with, such as famine, flood, and drought.
2 The text suggests the problem could be avoided by reducing the world's consumption of fossil fuels. We could improve the situation by using our cars less, not burning coal, not wasting energy.
3 Egypt could be the worst affected country. If the Nile Delta were flooded, 16% of its population would lose their homes. The area of desert would increase, and it would suffer water shortages.
4 The forecasts on climate change for the next hundred years are probably very reliable as they are based on studies and estimates made by climatology experts.

Focus on vocabulary

1
1 k	4 f	7 e	10 i
2 c	5 g	8 d	11 j
3 h	6 a	9 l	12 b

2
1 crop
2 shrinks
3 estimate
4 resort
5 sank
6 projected
7 forecast
8 appeal
9 impact
10 the norm
11 shortage
12 decline

Reference words

2 fossil fuels
3 The UN's Intergovernmental Panel on Climate Change
4 Venice; the Nile Delta and Thessaloniki
5 the beach resorts

Vocabulary

Topic vocabulary: the environment

1
1 ACID
2 POLLUTE
3 CLIMATE
4 RAINFOREST
5 OZONE
6 FOSSIL
7 AEROSOL

2
1 cut down: rainforests
2 dump: nuclear waste
3 kill: endangered species
4 protect: the environment; endangered species
5 recycle: bottles
6 use up: non-renewable resources

3 1 Rainforests are being cut down because of world demand for expensive woods like ebony.
  2 Possible answers: the rhino, the tiger, the whale, etc.
  3 Nuclear waste is dumped in landfill sites and in the sea. This a concern because the containers could leak, allowing the waste to contaminate the land and the sea.
  4 Coal, oil, and gas are non-renewable sources of energy. The sun and wind and water can provide us with renewable sources of energy.
  5 Many things can be recycled, e.g. clothes, paper, metal.

Phrasal verbs: *bring* + particle

1 1 brought together
  2 brought out
  3 bring down
  4 brought about
  5 bring in

2 1 brought down
  2 brings together
  3 are bringing / are going to bring out
  4 bring in
  5 is bringing / has brought about

Word-building

1

Verb	Noun
consume	consumption
emit	emission
reduce	*reduction*
deteriorate	deterioration
predict	*prediction*

2 1 predictions
  2 consumption
  3 emitted
  4 deteriorating
  5 reduction

Grammar

1 Futures review

will

2 g 3 e 4 a 5 f 6 b 7 h 8 d

will and *going to*

1 1 I'm going to
  2 will be
  3 He'll miss
  4 won't mind
  5 We're going to crash
  6 will be
  7 It's going to rain.
  8 You'll be
  9 he's going to be
  10 won't get married; will just live

2 1 am going to give up; am going to get fit; am not going to make
  2 will meet; will take

  3 Are you going to see; will pass on
  4 am going to fail
  5 will arrive; will get
  6 are going to have; will bring
  7 will you be; will be
  8 will come

2 Future continuous and Future perfect

1 1 will be lying; will be travelling
  2 will be swimming; will be typing
  3 will be dancing; will be watching
  4 will be enjoying

2 1 Will you have finished; will have written
  2 will have passed; will have taken
  3 won't have forgotten
  4 will have eaten

3 • We *will have put* men on Mars.
  • Society *will have become* more caring.
  • Medical science *will have found* a cure for baldness.
  • Most people *will be walking around* with at least one artificial part in their bodies.
  • Everyone *will be using* plastic cards not cash.
  • We *will have discovered* intelligent life elsewhere in the universe.
  • Computers *will have changed* our lives completely
  • We *will be paying* taxes for clean air just like we do for clean water.

Future forms

1 A: What *are you going to do* with your free time now that you've retired?
  B: I think I'*ll take up* a new hobby.
  A: *Are you going to come* down to the gym with me?
  B: No. I'*m not going to do* anything too energetic. Maybe I'*ll take* swimming lessons.
  A: I'*ll teach* you to swim if you like.
  B: How long *will it take* me to learn?
  A: Not long. You'*ll be swimming* like a fish in three months at most.
  B: All right. I'*ll take up* your offer.
  A: I'*ll send* you the bill. Just joking!

2 A: What *are we going to do* this evening?
  B: Well I don't know about you but I'*m going to watch* TV. Brazil are playing Italy.
  A: Oh, no. Not football. I think I'*ll go out*.
  B: The match *will have finished* by 10. We could go out then.
  A: OK. But I'*m not going to watch* it.

3 A: *Will you have done* all the housework by the time I get home from work?
  B: I'*ll have cleaned* the bathroom. I'll probably *be making* the dinner at 6 o'clock. You'*ll be* just in time to help me!

3 The language of contrast

1 1 In spite of / Despite the fact that people nowadays have more free time, they do not always spend it wisely.

  People nowadays have more free time. However, they do not always spend it wisely. / People nowadays have more free time. They do not always spend it wisely, however.

  2 Instead of doing something useful with their time, they waste it.

  3 Whereas / while some people believe that doing nothing is a sin, others believe that it is good for us to 'switch off'.

  Some people believe that doing nothing is a sin. On the other hand others believe that it is good for us to 'switch off'.

  4 They believe that relaxation is the key to good health rather than physical exercise. / They believe that relaxation, rather than physical exercise, is the key to good health.

  5 'Switching off' is not easy. In fact, many people find it impossible.

  6 We may think that we are relaxed. However, our muscles are tense and our brains still active. / We may think that we are relaxed. Our muscles are tense and our brains still active, however.

  Although / Even though we may think that we are relaxed, our muscles are tense and our brains still active.

  7 Instead of watching so much television, we should practise a form of meditation, like yoga.

2 1 rather than
  2 although / even though
  3 instead of
  4 In spite of
  5 but
  6 however
  7 even though / although
  8 not
  9 In fact

Writing

Topic sentences

1 The streets of the capital, which are attractive because they are scruffy.

  The fact that it is a real place, not a place that exists simply for tourists.

  The golden beaches.

  The price – it is cheap.

2 a 3 b 6 c 5 d 2 e 1
  The extra sentence is 4.

3 **Paragraph 1:** … what is it about Zanzibar that makes it seem so exotic …

  Paragraph 2: Although there are a few smart hotels … there are no magnificent buildings; drab …; run-down and shabby …; a delightful maze of scruffy streets

Paragraph 3: … full of local people buying their daily necessities …; … the constant clatter of furniture being made …

Paragraph 4: Palm trees fringe the golden sands and sway gently in the breeze …; The roar of the waves …; An occasional fisherman strolls past …

Paragraph 5: Lighting comes from a storm lamp and a ceiling fan moves air lazily round the room.; $16 a night

4 From the definition of the word *maze* we can suppose that the streets were narrow and winding and you could easily get lost in them.

We may make several interpretations of the word *riot* from its definition: each stall might have had a lot of things on display; there may have been lots of stalls; the stalls may have been rather disorganized.

Unit 4

Reading

As you read

1 The writer's father was down-to-earth and got on well with children. The mother was different from the other mothers. She wasn't interested in her house and seemed severe.

2 The house was like this because the boy's mother wasn't interested in it and because she never threw or gave anything away.

Understanding the text

1 She was not interested in looking after the house; she didn't make it into a home. She was not interested in material possessions like new furniture, only in things of sentimental value.

2 The writer's mother possibly didn't want anyone to know her age because her husband was younger than her and she didn't want to admit to this.

3 A bird when resting stands on one leg; it is always ready to fly away. They were never really settled in one place but were always ready to move on.

4 She was very sentimental because she never threw anything away.

She had probably loved her own mother a lot. (She has kept the coat left to her.)

She had been a nurse. (The books were heavily underlined; there was a diploma.)

She was Jewish. (She had a Hebrew Bible.)

She had lived with an aunt. (Maybe she had been orphaned and brought up by her.)

She liked reading. (She had lots of books.)

5 He wasn't allowed to celebrate his birthday and his home wasn't very comfortable. He didn't seem to mind this. He doesn't make any comments about the house. He didn't seem to mind not having birthdays – he *prided himself on not having them*. However, he didn't like it when she called him in when he was playing with the other boys.

Focus on vocabulary

1 1 boast
   2 foolish
   3 neat
   4 sharply
   5 odds and ends
   6 shabby
   7 heaps
   8 tattered
   9 bundle
   10 humiliated

2 1 heap
   2 neat
   3 boasting
   4 foolish
   5 shabby
   6 sharply
   7 odds and ends
   8 bundles
   9 humiliated
   10 tattered

Vocabulary

Phrasal verbs: *go, give, throw, put, take + away*

1 1 c   4 e   7 b   10 g
   2 f   5 a   8 i
   3 h   6 j   9 d

2 1 put … away
   2 going away
   3 took … away
   4 giving … away
   5 take … away
   6 would give … away
   7 took … away
   8 goes away
   9 threw away
   10 puts … away

Topic vocabulary: ways of looking

1 1 glance
   2 watch
   3 stare
   4 glimpse
   5 peer
   6 gaze

2 2 ✔
   3 peered

4 ✔
5 gazes
6 watched
7 glanced

Word-building

1 self-discipline
2 self-defence
3 self-catering
4 self-centred
5 self-service
6 self-contained
7 self-employed

Grammar

1 Rules, needs, duties and advice review

1 want to
2 should/ought to
3 have (got) to
4 want to
5 must
6 shouldn't/oughtn't to
7 have to/need to
8 must
9 has to
10 do you have to
11 should/ought to
12 shouldn't

2 Prohibition/no obligation

1 mustn't speak
2 don't have to come
3 didn't need to type
4 mustn't take
5 needn't have made
6 needn't have hurried
7 doesn't have to come
8 didn't need to eat
9 mustn't swim
10 don't have to let me know

Mixed patterns

Possible answers

1 You *should* go to an English-speaking country; you *should* enrol at a good language school.

2 I *need to* have at least 8 hours' sleep a night.

3 You *mustn't* smoke in all public buildings and on public transport; you *mustn't* make a noise in libraries.

4 You *should* bring lots of T-shirts, shorts and a swimming costume. You *needn't* bring an umbrella, a jacket, a lot of sweaters.

Or the opposite if it is cold in your country in August.

5 School: We *have to* wear a uniform; we *mustn't* be rude to the teachers; we *mustn't* run in the corridors; we *mustn't* eat in class.

University: We *must* attend 80% of classes; we *must* hand our work in on time.

Work: We *mustn't* smoke except in specially designated areas; we *have to* be on time; we *mustn't* use the phone for personal calls.

6 I *have to* make my bed and keep my bedroom tidy. I *have to* lay the table, clear the table and wash up. I *don't have to* wash my own clothes or cook meals.

3 Speculating about past events

1 1 He might have lost his job.
   He might have slept badly.

   2 She might not have been invited.
   She might have been ill.
   She might have forgotten.

   3 She might have bought it from her.
   Mandy might have lent it to her.
   It might not have been Susan.

2 2 a He might have forgotten.
   b He can't have forgotten.
   c His boss must have asked him to work late.

   3 a She must have gone to bed late.
   b She can't have gone to bed late.
   b She might not have slept well.

   4 a She might have lost it.
   b Her fiancé must have broken off their engagement.
   c She can't have finished with him.

Writing

Making writing interesting (2): adjectives, describing a person

1 Nick is a good friend of the writer's. She likes his looks, his gentleness, and his ability to listen.

2 a worried
  b ancient tweed
  c old blue
  d dark-blue woollen
  e untidy
  f beautiful
  g blond curly
  h piercing blue
  i long straight
  j high
  k thin-lipped and straight

Descriptive adjectives

Hair
ginger   shoulder-length   wavy

Nose
crooked   turned up

Mouth
full-lipped   wide

Eyes
large   hazel   sad   smiling   wide

Order of adjectives

* *Opinion* adjectives go before *fact* adjectives:
  beautiful blue eyes.

* Adjectives of *size* and *length* usually go before adjectives of *shape* and *width*:
  long straight nose;
  big round eyes.

* When describing hair the order is either *length* + *colour* + *type* or *length* + *type* + *colour*:
  long blond curly hair;
  long curly blond hair.

  straight usually comes <u>before</u> colour:
  straight brown hair.

* When describing objects and clothes the usual order is:
  size + *age* + *colour* + *origin* + *what made of* + noun:
  dark-blue woollen sweater;
  ancient tweed jacket

  It is unusual to have more than three adjectives before any noun.

1 The girl had *gorgeous ginger shoulder-length* hair.
2 Peter has *short brown wavy* hair.
3 The woman had *smiling hazel* eyes.
4 ✔
5 She was wearing a *short white cotton* dress.
6 He had on an *attractive new pink* shirt.

Describing character

1 1 d   2 a   3 b   4 c   5 e

Unit 5

Reading

As you read

1 True.
2 False. They were originally made for American gold prospectors.
3 False. Denim is the name of the kind of cloth.
4 True.
5 False. Most jeans are bought by people in the 45–54 age group.
6 True.

Comprehension

a 7   b 4   c 1   d 8   e 6   f 2   g 5
The extra sentence is 3.

Focus on vocabulary

1 1 hardwearing
   2 tough
   3 decade
   4 lay off
   5 cut
   6 respectable
   7 yearn
   8 ban

2 1 decades
   2 tough
   3 banned
   4 to cut
   5 yearned
   6 respectable
   7 laid off
   8 hard-wearing

Vocabulary

Topic vocabulary: employment

1/2

Verb	Noun
promote	promotion
employ	(un)employment
	employer
	employee
retire	retirement
resign	resignation
apply	application
	applicant

3 1 got
   2 has been looking for
   3 has sent off
   4 am going to hand in / am handing in

4 1 part-time
   2 full-time
   3 trade union
   4 strike
   5 sack; fire
   6 redundant

5 1 made redundant
   2 applied
   3 part-time
   4 went on strike
   5 trade union

Phrasal verbs: *get* + particle

1 1 Get over sth: recover from an illness or a shock
   2 Get out of sth: avoid doing sth
   3 Get round to (doing) sth: do sth after a long delay
   4 Get through sth: consume
   5 Get sb down: depress
   6 Get by: manage
   7 Get round sb: persuade sb to let you do or have sth
   8 Get sth across: communicate an idea to others

2 1 got round to
   2 getting over
   3 get round
   4 gets ... across
   5 get ... down
   6 got out of
   7 get through
   8 get by

Grammar

1 Conditionals review

The lottery
1 would do; won
2 win/won; will/would solve
3 had kept; would have won
4 remember; buy

Holidays
1 go away; go
2 had; would spend
3 hadn't broken; would have gone
4 will … go; is

Relationships
1 hadn't gone; wouldn't have met
2 meet; is
3 would … get married
4 don't go out; won't meet

Work
1 had had; would have set up
2 get; work
3 hadn't insisted; wouldn't have applied
4 got/get; would be/will

2 The verb *wish*
1 hadn't gone
2 didn't have to
3 would stop
4 could
5 had been able to
6 were (was); didn't have to
7 wouldn't keep
8 lived
9 had told
10 would tell

3 Mixed conditional sentences
2 hadn't been burgled; wouldn't have moved
3 hadn't invested; wouldn't have lost
4 hadn't lost; wouldn't be; wouldn't be cleaning
5 hadn't had; wouldn't be packing
6 wouldn't have left; hadn't got
7 hadn't spent; wouldn't be driving

4 Past verbs with present or future meaning

It's time
2 It's time he started looking for another job.
3 It's time John had/got his hair cut.
4 It's time Julie had a holiday.
5 It's time you got up.

I'd rather
2 I'd rather you did this photocopying.
3 I'd rather we didn't postpone the meeting.
4 I'd rather you sent it yourself.
5 I'd rather you didn't tell him.

Writing

Connecting ideas (1)

1 They have the following in common: they are both tall, blond and blue-eyed, they both like sailing and fishing, and they both enjoy being twins but dislike it when people treat them as if they were one person.
   They are different in the following ways: Scott hated violence, but James quite liked it; James refused to fight, but Scott often got into fights.

2/3
Contrast
But; however; by contrast; apart from; in comparison; on the other hand
Additional
Besides; as well as; on the one hand
Example
For instance; for example
Generalization
On the whole; by and large; in general

4
1 but
2 By contrast/In comparison
3 Apart from
4 As well as
5 In general/By and large/On the whole
6 however
7 for example/for instance
8 On the one hand; on the other hand

Unit 6

Reading

As you read
1 True.
2 False. They do their best work in their early twenties.
3 True.
4 False. Oil rig divers peak around 43.
5 True.
6 True.

Understanding the text
1 As we get older we get wrinkles and other small marks on our face; our complexions are less clear; some people lose their hair; we may put on weight and become fat unless we exercise regularly.
2 She wants the article to appear factual. The quotations are from people who are experts in their fields.
3 Goalkeepers don't need to be physically as fit – footballers need to be very fit because of the amount of running they have to do. Agility is more important for a goalkeeper, as well as experience and confidence.
4 *Surprisingly* (line 65)

– the writer is surprised that oil rig divers peak so late.
Fortunately (line 95)
– the writer is pleased that there are exceptions to the rule.
Thankfully (line 105)
– the writer is pleased/relieved that age is not a barrier to what you want to do. Her relief suggests that she herself is in her thirties or older.

Focus on vocabulary

1 at the height (paragraph 4);
at the summit (paragraph 6);
at their best (paragraph 11);
at the top (paragraph 12)

2 1 assume
2 bonus
3 quit
4 cram
5 work under pressure
6 in-depth
7 be geared towards
8 adverse
9 moan

3 1 quit
2 adverse
3 assume
4 cram
5 moan
6 work under pressure
7 in-depth
8 is geared towards
9 bonus

Vocabulary

Word-building

1/2

Verb	Noun
combine	combination
experience	experience
perfect	*perfection*
prove	*proof*
require	*requirement*
dedicate	dedication
vary	*variety*
	variation

3 1 requirements
2 vary; variation
3 combination
4 proof; prove
5 combines
6 required
7 experienced
8 variety
9 dedicate; dedication
10 perfect; perfection
11 experience

Topic vocabulary: stages of life

1 Wordsearch

```
T A D O L E S C E N C E
O E Q R S D P E P A T L
D P E N S I O N R R V D
D R M O L M T B E E C E
L O A D R O S A G T U R
E M R P L A G Y N I L L
R O R L A T E E A R L Y
Z T I X L K G I N E T R
F I A T E E N S T M O S
R O G A L T O U T E R T
D N E F I G S U H N I P
A R D I V O R C E T A M
```

1 promotion
2 marriage
3 late
4 early
5 mid
6 teens
7 pregnant
8 elderly
9 retirement
10 toddler
11 adolescence
12 spots
13 pension
14 divorce

2
1 retirement
2 promotion
3 pregnant
4 marriage
5 pension
6 divorce
7 Adolescence

Phrasal verbs: *bring up, make up, take up, break down*

1
1 break down
2 bring up
3 take up
4 break down
5 make up
6 bring up
7 make up
8 take up

2
1 has broken down
2 took up
3 was brought up
4 make up
5 takes up
6 make up
7 broke down
8 bringing … up

3 Personal answers

Grammar

1 Present perfect review

1
1 Have you heard
2 has she known
3 met
4 was
5 Have you met
6 has told
7 did you see
8 saw
9 went out
10 said

2
1 phoned
2 have split up
3 have had/had
4 happened
5 started
6 said
7 Have you bought
8 have … sent

2 Present perfect continuous (1)

1 I've been running; I've run
2 She's broken
3 has visited
4 I've had
5 I've made
6 I've been making
7 have you smoked/have you been smoking
8 has always been
9 I've studied/I've been studying
10 haven't spoken
11 I've stayed/I've been staying
12 Have you finished
13 I've been saving
14 I've been meaning
15 She's had

3 Present perfect continuous (2)

2 I've been wondering what to do with all these old clothes.
3 I've been wishing I'd told you the real reason.
4 I've been wanting to ask where you got that dress.
5 I've been meaning to tell you.
6 I've been intending to write.
7 I've been looking forward to seeing you again.
8 I've been wishing I'd told you the truth.
9 I've been wanting to know why Mary and Richard split up.
10 I've been wondering how to convince her I'm sorry.
11 I've been meaning to clear out that cupboard.
12 I've been meaning to ask (you) what you want for your birthday.

Past simple and Present perfect tenses

1 have you been doing
2 haven't written
3 have been
4 I've been looking
5 I've sent
6 have had
7 I've been
8 had
9 haven't heard
10 I've been learning
11 haven't crashed
12 have been meaning
13 Did you buy
14 I've been writing
15 I've been invited

Writing

Expressing an opinion: adverbs (2)

1 3: It is difficult to decide on a legal age for doing certain activities.

2 1/2 **This is my personal opinion**
As far as I'm concerned;
In my opinion; In my view
I am sure of the facts / I agree with the facts Of course; Certainly
I am less sure of the facts Apparently
I am surprised Curiously; Strangely
I am not surprised Needless to say
I am pleased Thankfully
I am not pleased Sadly

3 b Fortunately/Thankfully, it didn't rain as I had forgotten to take my umbrella.
c Strangely/Curiously/Surprisingly, Rachel doesn't resemble her twin at all.
d In my opinion/In my view/As far as I'm concerned/Personally, I think people should be allowed to vote when they are 16.
e Not surprisingly/Needless to say, Sue didn't invite Mark.
f As far as I know/Evidently/Apparently, you can get married in Scotland when you're 16.
g Not surprisingly/needless to say, John was late.
h In my opinion/In my view/As far as I'm concerned/Personally, I think smoking shouldn't be allowed on any flight.

Unit 7

Reading

As you read

1 True.
2 True.
3 False. They hallucinate and behave in an irrational way.
4 True.
5 False. The insulating properties of snow makes a fire unnecessary.

Focus on vocabulary

1
1 transform
2 severe
3 evolve
4 adapt

5 irrational
6 rucksack
7 dump
8 blizzard
9 spot
10 stumble
11 nuisance
12 go to great lengths
13 insulate
14 snug

2 1 dumped
2 evolved
3 insulates
4 adapted
5 severe
6 Blizzard
7 spot
8 nuisance
9 rucksack
10 snug
11 transform
12 went to great lengths
13 irrational
14 stumbled

Understanding the text

1 Human beings compensate for not being able to hibernate or grow extra hair in various ways. They wear extra clothing made of warm materials like wool. They cover their heads with hats (to prevent heat loss) and keep hands and feet warm with gloves and socks when they go out. They stay indoors more in winter than in summer; they eat hot food. They use sources of heat to keep warm (fires, central heating, etc.).

2 A person lost in the snow might make the following argument for getting rid of their cagoule: 'I'm hot. I don't need this' and for their boots: 'My feet are sore. These boots are heavy, uncomfortable. I'd be more comfortable/could walk more easily without them.'

3 Andy probably stayed in a snow-hole during the three days that the blizzard lasted. In this way he would have kept reasonably warm and conserved his energy.

4 Farmers would have to provide food for animals who normally graze on the grass. They would need to rescue any animals trapped in snowdrifts: they would need to check that none were missing. Snow can destroy fences, which would need to be rebuilt/repaired.

Pedestrians might need to clear the snow from paths leading to their houses. It is difficult to walk through snow – pavements might not be cleared.

For motorists, travel would be more difficult as roads would need to be cleared and driving conditions would be bad, with ice, blizzards, snowdrifts.

5 Nowadays we don't need to rely on the insulating properties of snow to keep our homes warm. Central heating provides warmth while insulating materials and double glazing on windows means that the heat doesn't escape.

Vocabulary

Topic vocabulary: weather

1 1 breeze … gale … hurricane
2 … fog
3 drizzle … downpour
4 … blizzard

2 2 dense; thick fog
3 light drizzle
4 thick snow
5 a light; gentle breeze
6 a torrential downpour
7 a cold; strong; gale-force wind

3 1 light/gentle breeze
2 thick snow
3 torrential downpour
4 cold wind
5 thick/dense fog
6 light drizzle

Topic vocabulary: ways of walking

1 1 b 2 d 3 a 4 c

2 1 marched
2 wandering
3 strolled
4 stumbled

Phrasal verbs: *come* + particle

1 1 d 2 f 3 c; e 4 b 5 g 6 a

2 1 came up against
2 ✔
3 ✔
4 came out
5 ✔
6 came across
7 come up

3 Personal answers

Word-building: -*ness* noun endings

1 illness
2 friendliness
3 kindness
4 carelessness
5 remoteness
6 loneliness
7 happiness
8 weakness

Grammar

1 *can, could, be able to* review

1 1 could
2 Can I
3 can't
4 have been able to
5 can
6 will be able to

2 1 Can; could; have you been able to
2 could; can't
3 Could/Can; can
4 have been able to
5 could; can't
6 to be able to

2 Ability and inability

1 1 Patrick succeeded in changing the wheel without any help.
2 I could swim when I was six but I couldn't swim underwater until I was eight.
3 Did you succeed in persuading Jason to come?
Were you able to persuade Jason to come?
4 Have you been able to meet your objectives?
Have you managed to meet your objectives?

2 1 could
2 be able to
3 could
4 couldn't
5 could
6 could
7 managed to
8 was able to
9 couldn't
10 could
11 succeeded

3 Articles

1 1 I've never been involved in *a* very serious car accident. *The* worst accident I had was when I was driving my brother Jim home in *the* fog. *The* car left *the* road and hit *a* tree. We both had to go to ✗ hospital but we were allowed to go ✗ home *the* same day. Jim had *a* broken leg and I had ✗ cuts and bruises.

2 I've always wanted to go to *the* United States. I'd like to travel to *the* east coast by ✗ plane and then hire *a* car. I'd drive west stopping at all *the* towns I passed on *the* way. I'd spend *the* night in *a* cheap motel just like *the* ones you see in *the* movies.

3 Everyone in my family has been to ✗ university. My brother and I both went to *the* University of Leeds. After finishing ✗ university, I went to ✗ college to train to be *a* teacher. I taught in *a* language school in *the* north of ✗ Turkey for *a* year.

4 ✗ Children love ✗ animals. ✗ Hamsters are ✗ good pets for ✗ young children. They are easy to look after. When I was young I had *a* cat. *The* cat's name was Smokey. It liked ✗ fish and ✗ milk. When it was *a* year old, it had ✗ kittens, which surprised my father as he had thought it was *a* male cat.

e There is *a* saying in English: 'An English-man's home is his castle.' Certainly, *the* English like to be private but there is a big difference between those who live in *the* south and those who live in *the* north. Not all ✗ English people are *the* same.

2 1 The hotter it gets the sleepier I feel.
2 The less she knows the better.
3 The sooner we finish the sooner we can go home.
4 The more you say the worse it is.
5 The more I earn the more tax I have to pay.

Writing

Cohesion

2 2 • Their location ✔
   50–100 km off the north-west coast of Scotland.
   • Their population ✔
   just under 30,000
   • Geographical features ✔
   beaches; rocky cliffs, and wild, rugged mountains
   • Names of the main towns ✔
   Stornoway
   • Why you should visit the islands ✔
   superb scenery; a paradise for naturalists and walkers
   • Exact details of how to get there ✗
   (This would be unusual in a preface, although general details might be given.)
   • The weather ✔
   May, June, July and August are the sunniest and driest months; average temperature then is 16–18 degrees centigrade. In winter it is very windy and not a lot of daylight.
   • Names of hotels and restaurants ✗
   (This information would be given in a separate chapter.)

3 Stornoway (line 6): This

The superb scenery (line 8):The islands are renowned for their superb scenery *which* includes silver …

May, June, July and August (line 13): The best time to visit the Outer Hebrides is between May and August, *which* are the sunniest and driest months.

The winds (line 23): They

The Outer Hebrides (line 26): They

different (line 28): individual; personal

Unit 8

Reading

As you read

1 The article mentions the following aspects: working with group members you don't know very well; the punishing schedule (a lot of travelling, lots of concerts, little time to relax); being treated like gods by fans but being bullied by managers; easy access to drink and drugs.

Other possible ideas not mentioned in the article are: you are often away from home (partners, children, family) for long periods of time; you are with the same group of people all the time; it is physically very demanding.

2 A therapist is someone who helps people deal with their problems. The therapist helps the members of the band by talking over possible problems they think they might have before the tour starts, and being available during the tour if any problems arise and they need someone to talk to.

Focus on vocabulary

1 1 cope; handle; tackle
2 key
3 ease
4 tension
5 bully
6 worship
7 make for
8 support
9 reluctant
10 fragile
11 turn against
12 devastating

2 1 fragile
2 was bullied
3 key
4 to cope
5 support
6 ease
7 makes for
8 devastating
9 tension
10 turned against
11 reluctant
12 worship

Understanding the text

1 Some of the pressures of fame are always being in the public eye; having no privacy; that people are always taking photos of you, asking you for autographs, etc. and that they expect you to behave in a particular way.

2 The writer thinks a rock star's lifestyle is *ridiculous* because it puts abnormal physical and mental demands on the person.

3 The managers who are having therapy probably want to keep it secret because they think they would be considered weak if people knew.

4 The expression 'If you can't stand the heat, get out of the kitchen' means if you can't take the pressure, leave the job. Record producers, uncaring managers, or other members of the group might say this.

5 They might become alcoholics or drug addicts or commit suicide. Some examples of people who have not been able to cope with the pressures of fame are: Michael Hutchence (INXS), who committed suicide, Jim Morrison (The Doors), who died from an alcohol and drug overdose, and Kurt Cobain (Nirvana), who committed suicide.

Synonyms

1 begin; commence
2 now and again
3 whole
4 afraid; concerned
5 as long as
6 expected
7 established
8 field
9 wonderful

Vocabulary

Topic vocabulary: music and musicians

1 1 e 2 d 3 a 4 h 5 f 6 c 7 b 8 g
2 drummer
 violinist
 guitarist
 pianist
3 1 tour
 2 live
 3 classical
 4 album
 5 composer
4 1 Orchestras; circuses; theatre groups; dance companies; art exhibitions.
 2 Recorded music.
 3–5 Personal answers

Phrasal verbs: *make* + particle

1 1 g 2 c 3 h 4 a 5 f 6 b 7 d 8 e
2 1 make out
 2 make up
 3 make for
 4 made up
 5 made out
 6 made for
 7 make up for
 8 made up

Grammar

1 Relative clauses review

1
1 … a village called Stanway, which …
2 The school which/that …
3 … a big hill, which …
4 … Emily, who …
5 … a big garden where …
6 Our parents, who both worked, …
7 … the reason why …
8 … Sunday, when …
9 My father, who was an only child …
10 … doing what …

No relative pronoun is needed in sentences 2 and 7.

2 Marley, *who was a Rastafarian,* wore his hair long in a distinctive style called 'dreadlocks'. This fashion, *which was followed by most Rastafarians,* was copied by young blacks and whites worldwide in the 1980s. The Rastafarians, *who worship the former Emperor of Ethiopia, Haile Selassie, as God,* are a religious group which originated in Jamaica. Marley's songs, *which often reflected his political beliefs,* popularized reggae music worldwide. Marley, *who was only 36 years old when he died of cancer,* had one of his biggest hits with the song 'No Woman No Cry'.

2 Relative clauses

1
2 … in *The Godfather Part 2 , for which* he won an Oscar.
3 … in the film *Raging Bull, for which* he had to put on 50 pounds.
4 De Niro helped Sylvester Stallone put on weight for his role in the thriller *Copland, in which* De Niro also stars.
5 The name *by which* Issur Danielovich Demsky is …
6 Kirk Douglas, *with whom* his son Michael is constantly compared, is best known …

2
2 … *Pretty Woman, which* Richard Gere starred *in* with Julia Roberts, is …
3 … divorced supermodel Cindy Crawford, *who* he had been married *to* for only three years, in 1994.
4 *Dancing with Wolves, which* Kevin Costner won several Oscars *for,* is …
5 *Waterworld, which* Costner invested a lot of his own money *in,* was …
6 The name *which* American actor and director Allan Stewart Konigsberg is better known *by* is …

3 Emphasizing words and structures

1
2 It may not seem like it sometimes but I do love you.
3 He isn't very good at cooking but he does try.

4 You obviously don't remember but I did tell you about it.
5 I did try to explain but he wouldn't believe me.
6 I really do think we should leave earlier.
7 Angela does look like her mother.
8 I did tell her you would be late.

2
2 My brother and I are very/really different.
3 Why ever/Why on earth don't you want to go?
4 The owners of the hotel themselves apologized to us.
5 What ever/What on earth have you done to your hair? It looks awful!
6 Kathleen Turner herself collected the award.
7 It's very/really strange you haven't met before.
8 We were very lucky indeed to get tickets. We were very/really lucky to get tickets.

Writing

Connecting ideas (2)

1 The best title is 2: The Chaplin Dynasty.

2 Charles Chaplin was born in 1889 <u>and</u> died in 1977 at the age of 88. <u>As well as</u> getting married three times, he had eleven children. Chaplin was well-known worldwide <u>both</u> as a comic actor <u>and</u> as a film director. <u>In addition to</u> the many short films he made, he <u>also</u> produced, acted in, and directed eleven full-length films, the last of which was *A Countess from Hong Kong* in 1967. Most of Chaplin's children and grandchildren have gone into some form of showbusiness <u>too</u>. Geraldine, Chaplin's eldest daughter, Christopher, his youngest son, and granddaughters Dolores and Carmen have all made acting their career while daughters Victoria, Annette and Josephine have worked in the theatre. To date Geraldine has had the most success. She has worked <u>not only</u> in Hollywood, where her most notable role was in the film *Doctor Zhivago*, <u>but also</u> in Europe. In the 70s she starred in many memorable films directed by the Spanish director Carlos Saura, who was her husband at the time. She has appeared in many films directed by the French film director Alain Resnais, <u>as well</u>. More recently she played the part of her own grandmother In Richard Attenborough's film about the life of her father, *Chaplin*.

3
2 My father's father, who was called John, was an excellent golfer and a talented artist too.
3 My father, whose name was Robert, was also good at painting.
4 He not only painted landscapes but (he) also (painted) portraits.

5 My mother was quite good at art as well, although she rarely had time for it.
6 My mother's brother was called James and the husbands of two of my mother's sisters were called James as well, which was rather confusing.

Unit 9

Reading

As you read

1 c   2 a   3 b   4 a   5 b

Focus on vocabulary

1
1 f	5 h	9 c
2 j	6 l	10 g
3 i	7 b	11 d
4 a	8 e	12 k

2
1 demanding
2 rate
3 tolerant
4 challenge
5 sponsor
6 revolutionary
7 conceded
8 project
9 quick-tempered
10 single-handed
11 room
12 took part in

Understanding the text

1 Presumably the price included the price of the kit, the satellite tracking systems and emergency beacons. It possibly also included the food and pump. It probably also had to cover the organizational costs, the cost of the two boats and crew which would accompany them, the cost of any possible rescue. They may have wanted to discourage people from entering – to keep the numbers down.

2 The Olympic rowers would be expert rowers and presumably would be very fit although we are not actually told <u>when</u> they were in the Olympics. It may have been a long time ago. They would not necessarily have any other advantages. They may only have experience of short races and probably have only rowed in rivers and lakes, not in the sea.

3 It will probably be easier for David: he's obviously very fit (his job would require it); he has had similar experience (he rowed across the Atlantic single-handed). Nadia has no experience at all and obviously had doubts because she thought of pulling out more than once.

4 They will be thinking a lot about their children the day before they go because there is the possibility that they might never see them again.

5 Examples: I mustn't lose my temper; I mustn't criticize/blame my partner for things; I must say sorry if I am at fault, etc.

It is very important that they are nice to each other on the trip because the boat is very small and there is nowhere to go if they have an argument. They must also work as a team so it is important that they get on.

Vocabulary

Topic vocabulary: travel

1 **board**
   bus/coach, helicopter, plane, ship, train
   disembark (from)
   plane, ship
   get in (to), get out (of)
   car/taxi, helicopter, rowing boat
   get on, get off
   bus/coach, horse, plane, ship, train

2 1 get on
   2 get off
   3 disembark/get out
   4 Getting into
   5 got into
   6 board

3 1 voyage
   2 travel
   3 journey
   4 trip
   5 excursions
   6 flight
   7 crossing

Collocations

1 **take** a bath, a break, a dislike, a look, a risk, an interest
   make a speech, a suggestion, (a car)
   run a bath, a car, a risk, in the family

2 1 make a suggestion
   2 took an interest
   3 makes a speech
   4 to run a car
   5 take a break
   6 Take a look
   7 run a bath
   8 are taking a risk
   9 runs in the family
   10 took a dislike

Phrasal verbs: *put off, pull out*

1 1 b 2 f 3 g 4 a 5 c 6 e 7 d

2 1 (to) pull ... out
   2 put off
   3 pulled out
   4 pulled out/have pulled out
   5 to put off
   6 put ... off
   7 puts ... off

Grammar

1 Time and reason clauses review

1 1 because
   2 As soon as/When
   3 As soon as/When/After
   4 as/since
   5 Since/As
   6 While
   7 Before
   8 until/After
   9 After/When

2 1 went
   2 go
   3 have booked/book
   4 start
   5 will have/has
   6 are able to
   7 are exercising/exercise
   8 came back

2 Participle clauses

1 1 Adventure training centres are designed for people *who want to do* outdoor activities.
   2 *When I arrived* at the adventure training centre, I was surprised to see that there were people of all ages there.
   3 *Because/As I hadn't been* to an adventure training centre before, I didn't know what to expect.
   4 *While I was putting on* my boots, I chatted to the person next to me.
   5 *Because/As he had been* three times previously, he was an expert.
   6 We left the changing rooms together and walked towards a group of people *who were standing* with the instructor.
   7 As I wanted to try canoeing, I was told to follow the path *which went* down to the river.
   8 *As/Because I hadn't been canoeing* before, I was a bit nervous.

2 1 *Fastening* my helmet under my chin, I suddenly remembered that I couldn't swim.
   2 *Making an excuse, I* ran back towards the main building.
   3 *Apologizing to the instructor, I* asked if I could try another activity.
   4 *Being afraid of heights, I wasn't* very keen to try mountain climbing.
   5 *Not being able to swim, I* couldn't go windsurfing either.
   6 *Having already paid in advance, I* felt I should do something.
   7 In the end, *deciding that outdoor sports were not for me, I* went home.

3 Cause and effect

1 ✔
2 make
3 cause
4 make
5 ✔
6 ✔
7 cause/bring about/result in/lead to
8 ✔

Writing
Connecting ideas (3)

1 **Possible answers**
He might have got on the wrong underground train. The underground trains might have been late. Perhaps he couldn't afford a taxi. He might have had to wait a long time for a taxi. Perhaps he missed his plane. Perhaps there was a problem with the flight. Perhaps it was delayed.

3 a 3 After (line 8)
   4 just before (11 p.m.) (line 9)
   5 before (line 10)
   6 Finally (at 2 a.m.) (line 12)
   7 By the time (line 15)
   8 the next morning (line 16)
   9 then (line 17)
   10 Straightaway (line 18)
   11 When (line 20)
   12 Up to that moment (line 22)
   13 Now (line 23)
   14 In the end (line 25)
   15 When (line 27)
   16 Over an hour later (line 31)
   17 At that moment (line 35)

 b at long last: *finally*
   the following (morning): *the next morning*
   at once/immediately: *straightaway*
   up to that point/until then: *up to that moment*
   just then: *at that moment*

4 1 Previously
   2 Meanwhile
   3 After a while
   4 Next time
   5 Afterwards

Unit 10
Reading
As you read

1 1 False. Children are able to lie by the time they are five.
   2 True.
   3 True.
   4 False. We try to but we find we can't.
   5 False. We gesticulate less.

2 1 c 2 e 3 a 4 g 5 f 6 b 7 d

Focus on vocabulary

1
1 reveal
2 work out
3 manipulate
4 contract
5 genuinely
6 symmetrical
7 pick out
8 gesticulate
9 blink
10 fiddle
11 charismatic
12 trustworthy

2
1 trustworthy
2 contract
3 blink
4 fiddle
5 charismatic
6 genuinely
7 reveal
8 work out
9 manipulate
10 symmetrical
11 pick out
12 gesticulating

Understanding the text

1 The ability to mind-read; having an honest face; being able to control your physical responses, e.g. heart rate, breathing, etc. if taking a lie-detector test; a lot of imagination; being able to control your body language; not regarding a lie as something wrong.

2 You might give a forced smile in the following situations: when you're having lots of photos taken or the photographer takes a long time to take the photo; when you're tired and haven't got the energy to smile; when you're introduced to someone you don't know who doesn't look very interesting or when you're being introduced to lots of people; when you don't win the prize/ get promotion etc. and your rival/ colleague does.
Some other kinds of smile are: a shy smile; an embarrassed smile; an apologetic smile; a smile of sympathy.

3 Personal answers.

Vocabulary

Topic vocabulary: crime

1
1 murder
2 forgery
3 fraud
4 blackmail
5 manslaughter

2
1 commit
2 criminal
3 jury
4 verdict
5 sentence
6 cell
7 convict

3
1 forgery
2 jury
3 committed
4 cells
5 criminals
6 verdict
7 fraud
8 sentence; murder
9 convicted; manslaughter
10 blackmail

Colour idioms

1 *blue*-eyed boy
2 in the *red*
3 out of the *blue*
4 in *black* and *white*
5 as *white* as a sheet
6 *Blue*-collar workers
7 *White*-collar workers
8 *green* with envy

Phrasal verbs: *work out, take in*

1 1 a 2 g 3 f 4 c 5 d 6 e 7 b

2
1 work out
2 take … in
3 work out
4 was taken in
5 working out
6 take in
7 take in

Grammar

1 Passives review

1
1 are sold
2 are paid
3 were boosted
4 are persuaded
5 are made
6 have not been affected

2
1 are reproduced/are being reproduced
2 are lost/are being lost
3 is represented
4 are bought
5 be bought
6 are being damaged
7 have been introduced
8 is organized

3
1 ~~by a judge~~
2 ✔
3 ~~by anyone~~
4 ~~by someone~~
5 ✔
6 ~~by the owner of the shop~~
7 ~~by the police~~

2 Passive constructions

2 Several buildings are reported to have been damaged. The town of Malibu is believed to have been the worst affected. There are thought to be no casualties.

3 The fire is believed to have started in the basement. It is believed to have been started deliberately.

4 Two paintings by Renoir and one by Picasso are said to be missing. One of the robbers is believed to have been working in the museum as a security guard.

3 The pronoun *it*

1
2 It was my father who/that taught me to play the guitar, not my brother./It wasn't my brother who/that taught me to play the guitar, it was my father.
3 It wasn't Mary I told, it was Sharon./It was Sharon I told, not Mary.
4 It's the week after next that Damien is arriving, not next week./It's not next week that Damien is arriving, it's the week after next.
5 It was Pete who/that took the decision, not me./It wasn't me who/that took the decision, it was Pete.
6 It isn't the taste of garlic I dislike, it's the smell./It's the smell of garlic I dislike, not the taste.

2
2 It's good to talk.
3 It made me sad to see him go.
4 It was difficult to make the decision.
5 It hasn't been easy to give up smoking.
6 It takes just over an hour to get to Paris from here.

3
3 We thought it was a shame that not many people came to the party.
4 I find it impossible to study with the television on.
5 Nick thinks it is funny that I've taken up skiing.
6 I thought it unusual that she didn't phone me to tell me she would be late.
7 I found it hard to write with a broken finger.

Writing

Supporting statements

1 Probably not.

2 a 3   b 1   c 4   d 2

3
1 Internet introverts.
2 The Internet.
3 The dark side of the Internet.
4 Parents.

Reading

As you read

The two words not used are *awful*; *ash*.

When she saw her first volcanic eruption she was *screaming* probably with a mixture of excitement and fear.

Seeing her first eruption was the most memorable *experience* she has ever had.

The volcano sounded like a *waterfall* when it started to erupt.

The volcano *coughed* out the rocks.

They always visit volcanoes with *experts*.

Volcanoes are *unpredictable*. You never know when they are going to erupt.

Comprehension

a 8   b 5   c 1   d 7   e 4   f 9   g 2   h 6
The extra sentence is 3.

Focus on vocabulary

1 1 d   2 b   3 a   4 e   5 c   6 g   7 f

2 1 choked
    2 aware
    3 spit
    4 hooked
    5 inhaling
    6 impressed
    7 date

Understanding the text

1 Possible answers

He probably wanted to find out if she was interested in volcanoes first. Although he was immediately attracted to her, he would need to find out if she felt the same way about him before going on what would probably have been an expensive trip.

2 As these words are normally used to describe the actions of people or animals, their use means we see the volcano as a living creature.

3 This comment tells us that Donna likes and needs excitement. She probably finds ordinary, everyday life extremely boring.

Vocabulary

Topic vocabulary: geographical features

1 1 peak
    2 mountain
    3 waterfall
    4 field
    5 estuary
    6 bay
    7 forest
    8 valley
    9 hill
    10 harbour
    11 stream
    12 lake
    13 wood
    14 cliff
    15 river
    16 meadow
    17 path
    18 shore
    19 beach
    20 rocks

2 1 mountainous
    2 steep; rocky
    3 shallow; deep
    4 pebbly
    5 fertile; fast-flowing

Topic vocabulary: sounds people make

1 1 c   2 e   3 d   4 a   5 f   6 b

2 1 groan/sigh
    2 scream
    3 gasp
    4 yell
    5 sob
    6 sigh/groan
    7 groan/gasp
    8 scream

Word-building: *-able*

1 1 unpredictable
    2 reliable
    3 unrecognizable
    4 preferable
    5 unacceptable
    6 profitable
    7 washable
    8 enjoyable

2 The stress on the verbs is the same as the stress on the adjectives (suffixes are not usually stressed). The words which are different are *prefer* and *preferable*.

Phrasal verbs: *fall* + particle

1 *fall back on*   use for help because no other alternative is available
fall behind   fail to do sth quickly enough or on time
fall for   be strongly attracted to sb
fall out   stop being friends with sb
fall through   (of an arrangement or plan) fail to happen

2 1 fell for
    2 fell behind
    3 fall back on
    4 ✔
    5 fell through

Grammar

1 Causatives review

1 2 Get ... mended
    3 had ... shortened
    4 get/have ... dry-cleaned
    5 had/got ... cleaned
    6 has had/has ... tinted
    7 have/get ... decorated
    8 had/got ... cleaned
    9 had/got ... made
    10 to get/have ... pierced
    11 have/get ... converted; have/get ... installed

2 1 Have you had your hair cut?
    2 We are getting a burglar alarm fitted next week.
    3 We might have the house painted blue.
    4 Has Michael had his car fixed yet?
    5 I usually get my teeth polished every six months.

2 Causative verbs

1 1 broken into
    2 stolen/taken
    3 scratched
    4 broken
    5 let down
    6 smashed
    7 burgled
    8 stolen/taken

2 2 He had his car radio stolen/taken.
    3 He had the paintwork scratched.
    4 He had the aerial broken.
    5 He had his tyres let down.
    6 He had his windscreen smashed.
    7 Natalie has had her flat burgled three times this year.
    8 She's had the video stolen/taken each time.

3 Question tags

1 was she
2 doesn't she
3 wouldn't she
4 are they
5 is it
6 isn't it
7 didn't she
8 has she
9 don't they
10 aren't there
11 did it
12 will/would you
13 shall we
14 did he
15 didn't he
16 are they
17 will you
18 don't they
19 shall we
20 has it

Question tags and requests

3 You don't mind if I open the window, do you?
4 You can't give me a lift, can you?
5 You don't mind if I'm a bit late, do you?
6 You couldn't post this letter for me, could you?

Writing

Connecting ideas (4)

2 Cities are exciting places; living in a city is convenient; if you work in the city, you will save time on travel.

3 Then; Finally.

They are at the beginning of sentences and often, as here, at the beginning of paragraphs. It is usual to include each new idea in a separate paragraph. Note that they are always followed by a comma.

4 In the first place: *To begin with; Firstly*
Then: *Secondly (Thirdly, etc.)*
Finally: *Lastly*

Unit 12

Reading

As you read

1 False. It is only important to police officers when they are interrogating suspects in the interview room.
2 False. Police officers are trained not to pay attention to body language.
3 True.
4 False. If you walk too quickly and look too confident you could be stopped.
5 False. How we communicate is more important.
6 False. Some people may exaggerate their body language when they are lying but some people may do the opposite.

Focus on vocabulary

1 **Police officer**
1 judge
2 vital
3 unwilling
4 tips

Customs officer
1 spokesperson
2 single out
3 smugglers
4 target

Job interviewer
1 first impressions
2 overall
3 exaggerate
4 static

2 1 spokesperson
2 smugglers
3 judge
4 exaggerating
5 first impression
6 vital
7 overall
8 tip
9 unwilling
10 target
11 single out
12 static

Understanding the text

1 They give the police officer the impression that they have committed a crime.
2 The writer says *Sadly* possibly because it would be useful to know this information if you were ever questioned.
3 A smuggler might pass through customs dressed as a nun because they might think that nuns (as members of a religious group) would be less likely to be stopped. Also, they could hide a lot of things in the long, loose-fitting clothing which nuns wear.
4 It is important to look smart at a job interview because appearance, body language, and clothes make up over 50% of the overall impression.
5 The interviewer who lay on the floor was possibly looking for someone adventurous, adaptable, prepared to take a risk, not afraid of making a fool of themselves. The main advantage is that it would save a lot of time.

Vocabulary

Topic vocabulary: the body

Collocations

1 1 i 2 h 3 f 5 e 6 c 7 b 8 d 9 a

2 2 blow their nose.
3 nod your head.
4 clear your throat.
5 cross their legs.
6 shake your head.
7 raise their eyebrows.
8 shrug your shoulders.
9 bite their nails.

Phrasal verbs: three-part verbs

1 1 has gone down with
2 face up to
3 go along with
4 catch up on
5 looks up to

2 1 to catch up on
2 go along with
3 looks up to
4 has gone down with
5 to face up to

Word-building

1 disappearance
2 appearance
3 impression
4 impressive
5 impressively
6 communication
7 communicative
8 offenders
9 offence
10 increasing
11 increasingly
12 unwilling
13 willingly
14 attractions
15 attractive

Grammar

1 Reported speech review

1 2 Amy asked Sally how many job applications she had sent off.
3 Amy said that she had sent off ten and that she had an interview the next/following day.
4 Sally asked Amy what she was going to wear.
5 Amy said she thought she would wear her navy suit and asked Sally if she could borrow her white blouse.
6 Sally said it was at the dry-cleaner's and asked Amy if she would take the job if they offered it to her.
7 Amy said she probably would if they offered her a decent salary.

2 2 'How did the interview go, Amy?' Sally asked.
3 'I was very nervous,' Amy said.
4 'I don't think I'll get the job because they want someone who can speak Spanish,' Amy said.
5 'Will you be disappointed if you don't get the job?' Sally asked.
6 'I've got an interview for a job in London next week, which I'm more interested in,' Amy said.

2 Reporting verbs

1 2 Before I left for the airport, my friend advised me not to take anything into the UK that I shouldn't.
3 He warned me not to try to take in any extra alcohol or cigarettes because the customs officers at Heathrow were very strict.
4 He insisted that it wasn't worth the risk and that I could be sent to prison.
5 I decided I would risk taking an extra carton of cigarettes.
6 The customs officer asked if/whether I had anything to declare.

7 He asked me to open my case.

8 He instructed me to open the carrier bag, too.

9 I argued that I hadn't known I could only bring in one carton of cigarettes.

10 I admitted that it had been stupid of me not to check.

11 The customs officer ordered me to go with him.

2 1 Keith suggested (that) we (could) buy Katie a book for her birthday.

Keith suggested (that) we bought Katie a book for her birthday.

Keith suggested buying Katie a book for her birthday.

2 Karen suggested (that) we get her a CD.

Karen suggested (that) we got her a CD.

Karen suggested getting her a CD.

3 David suggested (that) we ask her what she wanted.

David suggested (that) we asked her what she wanted.

David suggested asking her what she wanted.

3 Infinitives and gerunds after verbs

1 liking
2 to get
3 to agree
4 to type
5 to admit; working
6 to take
7 taking
8 to work
9 having
10 to reach
11 to work/working
12 to work/working
13 to ask
14 to ignore

Infinitives and gerunds with a change of meaning

1 getting
2 playing
3 to remind
4 telling
5 going
6 to explain
7 to tell
8 telling
9 to send
10 marrying
11 to have
12 eating

Writing

Register

1 Suggested answers

1 Member of the interview panel to Personnel Department. Formal language.

2 Same person or another member of the interview panel to a friend who used to work for the same company. Informal language.

3 The interviewee to a friend. Informal language.

2 Informal language: answers from:

personal tone
  I thought we'd never find …

contracted verb forms
  I'd really like the job 'cos they're …

phrasal verbs
  take over [Text 2]

words left out (e.g. personal pronouns)
  (I'll) See you soon.

slang or colloquial expressions
  fingers crossed

use of questions
  you remember June, don't you?

use of exclamation marks (!)
  Better late than never!!!

Formal language

1 longer sentences
  Most of the sentences in Text 1

2 impersonal tone
  Text 1, sentence 1

3 full verb forms
  Ms Mayall is presently working …

3 1 Thank you
2 post
3 would like
4 attend
5 ensure
6 receive
7 employer
8 that date
9 advise us
10 We look forward to seeing you on the 19th.

4 1 It's been ages since I've written, I know. Sorry!
2 do you think you could write me
3 I've got an interview
4 they want my references in
5 Thanks a million.

UNIVERSITY PRESS

Great Clarendon Street, Oxford OX2 6DP

Oxford University Press is a department of the University of Oxford.
It furthers the University's objective of excellence in research, scholarship, and education by publishing worldwide in

Oxford New York

Athens Auckland Bangkok Bogotá Buenos Aires Calcutta Cape Town Chennai Dar es Salaam Delhi Florence Hong Kong Istanbul Karachi Kuala Lumpur Madrid Melbourne Mexico City Mumbai Nairobi Paris São Paulo Shanghai Singapore Taipei Tokyo Toronto Warsaw

with associated companies in Berlin Ibadan

Oxford and Oxford English are registered trade marks of Oxford University Press in the UK and in certain other countries

© Oxford University Press 2000

Database right Oxford University Press (maker)

First published 2000
Second impression 2000

Designed by Holdsworth Associates, Isle of Wight

ISBN 0 19 433087 7

Printed in Hong Kong

The authors and publisher are grateful to those who have given permission to reproduce the following extracts and adaptations of copyright material: p.6 'White riot' by Michael Hanlon. Appeared in *The Independent* 5 July 1997. p.11 'Woman foils sharks in record swim to Florida' by David Adams. Appeared in *The Times* 13 May 1997 © Times Newspapers Limited, 1997. p.12 'Sungura' by Tracey Lloyd © Tracey Lloyd 1989. Reprinted by permission of The Maggie Noach Literary Agency. p.18 'Could global warming sink your holiday plans?' by Nicholas Schoon. Appeared in *The Independent* 13 November 1997. p.23 'The life of spice' by Richard Holledge. Appeared in *The Independent* 3 January 1998. p.24 'Mother' from Alien Son by Judah Waten, reproduced by permission of HarperCollins Publishers. p.29 Rainforest by Jenny Diski, published by Methuen. Reproduced by permission of Random House UK Limited. p.30 'Death of denim?' by Anna Pukas. Appeared in *The Daily Express* 19 July 1997. p.36 'When you hit your career peak' by Virginia Blackburn. Appeared in *The Daily Express* 3 October 1996. p.42 Savage Skies, Granada Television booklet published by Granada Television Ltd. p.47 25 Walks: The Western Isles by June Parker, 1996. Reproduced by permission of The Stationery Office, Edinburgh. p.48 'On the road, on the couch' by Peter Coleman, 29 November 1997 © *The Guardian*. p.54 'Couple set fair for rowing Atlantic without rowing' by Mike Rowbottom. Appeared in *The Independent* 9 October 1997. p.60 'Who's telling porkies' by Sanjida O'Connell. Appeared in *Focus* October 1997 edition, and reproduced by permission of Gruner & Jahr (U.K.) Partners. p.65 'Virtually no life at all' by Michael Shulman. Appeared in *The Guardian* 14 May 1996 © *Los Angeles Times*, reproduced with their permission. p.66

Savage Earth: The Book of the ITV Series' by Alwyn Scarth (1997). Reproduced by permission of HarperCollins Publishers Ltd.

Illustrations by:
Phil Disley pp.1, 27, 39, 58, 75
Emma Dodd/Black Hat Illustration pp.15, 28, 62, 76
Clive Goodyer pp.50, 70
Madeleine Hardie pp.8, 16, 26, 56, 64, 74 .
Stephanie Hawken pp.12
Claire Littlejohn pp.68
Gilly Marklew pp.24, 25
David Semple pp.44, 56
Tim Slade pp.17, 47
Technical Graphics Dept, OUP pp.11, 18, 54

The Publishers would like to thank the following for their kind permission to reproduce photographs and other copyright material: Associated Press p.18 (flooded Venice); Bos'un pp.33 (R D Battersby/woman in 40s), 48 (R D Battersby), 63 (R D Battersby/trainers); Colorific p.42 (Bryan and Cherry Alexander/Igloo); Focus p.60;The Guardian p.48 (Martin Argles/Jacky Gerald); Harper Collins pp.66, 67 (Donna and Steve); Image Bank pp.36 (Derek Berwin/Police woman, Peter G Bowater/Divers), 42 (Marvin E Newman/ House), 63 (Eric Berrue/Perfume), 72 (Paul Simcock); The Independent p.55 (Robert Hallam); The Kobal Collection pp.30 (James Dean), 31 (Goldie Hawn), 52 (Michael Douglas); Andrew Lambert p.33 (Young woman); PA News pp.36 (Judge, Runner, Naomi Campbell), 51, 52 (Robert De Niro, Kirk Douglas), 53 (Charlie Chaplin, Geraldine Chaplin, Carmen Chaplin); Science Photo Library pp.35 (Alex Bartel/Twins), 67 (Simon Fraser/Volcano); Stock Shot p.42 (Jess Stock/Snowhole); Telegraph Colour Library pp.6 (VCL), 23 (Richard Dobson), 31 (VCL/Paul Viant/Young people in Jeans, Masterfile/Cowboy), 73 (Daniel Allan/Customs Officer, Geoff Tompkinson/woman interviewer); Tony Stone pp.31 (Moggy/Jeans), 33 (Charles Thatcher/older man, Dale Durfee/young man), 36 (David Madison/Goal keeper), 46 (Peter Dean), 70 (Dale Durfee/girl, Christopher Arneseni/Sydney Harbour), 71 (John Lamb)